THE ROMANCE OF
TRISTRAM AND YSOLT

The Romance of

TRISTRAM & YSOLT

by Thomas of Britain

Translated from the

OLD FRENCH *and* OLD NORSE

by ROGER SHERMAN LOOMIS

PROFESSOR OF ENGLISH, COLUMBIA UNIVERSITY

NEW REVISED EDITION

COLUMBIA UNIVERSITY PRESS

NEW YORK 1951

COPYRIGHT 1923, E. P. DUTTON & COMPANY

COPYRIGHT 1931, 1951, COLUMBIA UNIVERSITY PRESS

REVISED EDITION, 1931

NEW REVISED EDITION, 1951

PUBLISHED IN GREAT BRITAIN, CANADA, AND INDIA
BY GEOFFREY CUMBERLEGE
OXFORD UNIVERSITY PRESS, LONDON, TORONTO, AND BOMBAY

MANUFACTURED IN THE UNITED STATES OF AMERICA

TO THE MEMORY OF

GERTRUDE SCHOEPPERLE LOOMIS

De s'amie a feite sa fame
Mes il l'apele amie et dame,
Que por ce ne pert ele mie,
Que il ne l'aint come s'amie,
Et ele lui tot autresi,
Con l'an doit feire son ami.
Et chascun jor lor amors crut.

CLIGÉS

The Romance of
TRISTRAM & YSOLT
by Thomas of Britain

Translated from the
OLD FRENCH *and* OLD NORSE
by ROGER SHERMAN LOOMIS
PROFESSOR OF ENGLISH, COLUMBIA UNIVERSITY

NEW REVISED EDITION

COLUMBIA UNIVERSITY PRESS
NEW YORK 1951

PUBLISHED IN GREAT BRITAIN, CANADA, AND INDIA
BY GEOFFREY CUMBERLEGE

OXFORD UNIVERSITY PRESS, LONDON, TORONTO, AND BOMBAY

MANUFACTURED IN THE UNITED STATES OF AMERICA

Preface

THE following translation is made, as the footnotes on pages 182, 184, 186, 221, 227, 238,
and 242 indicate, from two sources, the surviving
fragments of Thomas's romance in Anglo-Norman
and the Old Norse translation from Thomas made by
the monk Robert in 1226. The editions used have
been the standard *Roman de Tristan par Thomas*,
Vol. I, edited by J. Bédier for the Société
des Anciens Textes Français, and the *Tristansage*, edited by E. Kölbing. Of my text
practically three-tenths is translated from Thomas,
and the remainder from the Old Norse. I have pre-
ferred to follow the Old Norse Saga rather than M.
Bédier's reconstruction, which, while following the
Saga in the main, diverges from it frequently to follow the *Tristan* of Gottfried von Strassburg or to
make additions from the same source. My reason
for doing so is that of his divergences from the Saga
some I regard as doubtful, and that, while granting
that of his additions most are justified, I feel that
in the Saga we have at least a medieval work which
M. Bédier himself admits is "notre témoin le plus
sûre de Thomas." To be sure, I have not followed
the Saga in the episode (ch. LXXXVII) where
Kaherdin overtakes the Queen's cavalcade. When
we find in the scene just previous that the Saga omits

the important detail given by Thomas that Tristram and Kaherdin watched the cavalcade from a tree, and that *Sir Tristrem* and Gottfried supply a fairly harmonious alternative to the Saga's version, we must admit that here Brother Robert is at fault. At other points I have seen no compelling reason to hold that Gottfried gives us a safer guide than the Saga. We know, of course, that Brother Robert omitted much, and those omissions especially in his summary treatment of the potion and of the meeting at the fountain are to be deeply regretted, but in my opinion we may regard what the cleric has preserved as fulfilling M. Bédier's judgment that "Il n'invente guère, n'ajoute guère." Therefore, when we do not have Thomas's own work, I have contented myself with rendering the Saga's version.

My translation of both the Anglo-Norman and Old Norse texts is generally close and in large measure literal. I have allowed myself throughout the following deviations from the letter: I have introduced names where pronouns have been used with uncertain reference. I have not always observed the original sentence division, but have either telescoped sentences into one, or cut up one sentence into two or more. I have introduced conjunctions where the coherence of thought was obscure. In handling the Saga I have taken additional liberties. I have omitted the prologue by Brother Robert, announcing his authorship and the date of composition, and have condensed the first fifteen chapters, dealing with the loves of Tristram's parents. I regard Kanelangres as a corruption of Rivalon-Reis. I have invariably omitted the parenthetical "he said" or "she said" near the opening of every speech as not characteristic of Thomas's own usage. In ch. XXX I have represented Tristram as going alone on the voyage to Ireland for the reasons given by me in *The Modern Language Review*, XIV, p. 39. In ch. LXIX I have introduced a French couplet supplied by Gottfried, which doubtless he had taken over from Thomas. In chapters LVIII and LXXXII the broad remarks of the ladies have been toned down. In ch. LXXXV, I have omitted the sentence found in the Saga, p. 99, l. 10, as entirely superfluous. Finally, in ch. LXXXVII I have substituted a passage based on *Sir Tristrem*, ll. 3083–3124, for the version of the Saga, which on grounds stated above I regard as here corrupt.

My handling of Thomas's own lines has been as close as I could make it without obscurity. In two places where I have found it impossible to make sense of the text as given by M. Bédier, I have employed readings which I put forward in *The Modern Language Review*, XIV, p. 43. I have also followed Professor Hilka's suggestions in the *Zeitschrift für Französische Sprache und Literatur*, XLV, p. 40.

The Chertsey Tiles, which are reproduced in this volume, have been the subject of a study entitled *Illustrations of Romance on Tiles from Chertsey Abbey*, published by me as Number 2 of Volume II of the University of Illinois Studies in Language and Literature. The bibliography of Tristram illustrations there given should be supplemented by *Romanic Review*, VIII, p. 197, and *Burlington Magazine*, XLI, p. 54.

I wish to express my sense of indebtedness to Professor Charles Sears Baldwin for suggesting many improvements in the wording of the translation, and to Mr. J. R. Holliday for generously supplying me with the completed figure of Tristram offering the potion to Ysolt.

Columbia University   R. S. L.
July, 1931

Contents

INTRODUCTION   XV

THE ROMANCE OF TRISTRAM AND YSOLT   I

BIBLIOGRAPHICAL NOTE   291

The Chertsey Tiles

RIVALON RECEIVETH A MESSENGER   13

TRISTRAM PLAYETH CHESS WITH THE
                         NORSEMEN   21

TRISTRAM IS BROUGHT UNTO MARK   33

TRISTRAM HARPETH BEFORE MARK   37

THE PORTER OPENETH TO ROALD   41

TRISTRAM APPROACHETH DUKE MORGAN   48

DUKE MORGAN SMITETH TRISTRAM   53

TRISTRAM SLAYETH DUKE MORGAN   55

THE BARONS LAMENT FOR THEIR SONS   61

THE BARONS IMPLORE GOD'S PITY   62

MARK KISSETH TRISTRAM   67

MORHAUT WOUNDETH TRISTRAM   73

TRISTRAM SLAYETH MORHAUT   74

MORHAUT IS CARRIED TO THE STRAND   77

MARK VISITETH TRISTRAM   81

TRISTRAM HARPETH IN THE RUDDERLESS
                               BOAT   82

TRISTRAM TEACHETH YSOLT TO HARP   85

TRISTRAM ENCOUNTERETH THE DRAGON   100

TRISTRAM OFFERETH HIS GAGE TO GORMON   120

TRISTRAM OFFERETH THE GOBLET TO YSOLT   131

[xiii]

The Chertsey Tiles

YSOLT BECKONETH TO TRISTRAM 165

YSOLT VOYAGETH UNTO TRISTRAM 283

THE DIRGE IS SUNG OVER TRISTRAM 287

Introduction

HENRY II, King of England, was a man of iron. A tireless administrator, a fierce and relentless warrior, a despiser of softness, an avid imperialist, he kept the hundreds of restless barons in all his wide possesions in terror of him. Or.e only he met his match. The rival authority of R.me forced him to knuckle under. Henry's court was hardly a home for softness and romance.

Yet when in pursuit of his imperialistic calculations he acquired the province of Aquitaine in marriage, he received into the bargain the very embodiment of the romantic tendencies of the age in the person of the Duchess Eleanor. Her first husband, King Louis of France, had taken her religiously on the Crusades, but she had taken neither them nor him as religiously as he might have wished. She came back from them, the subject of exciting rumors of amours with princes both Christian and Saracen. Then after her separation from Louis, Bernard de Ventadour had sung of her some of the sweetest of troubadour lyrics. Eleanor brought with her to the fogs of London and the stark brutalities of Henry's court a breath from the olive gardens and vineyards of Languedoc, a glimpse of the opaline sea, a new idealism of love.

Henry appreciated literature in his own way. He realized with the true instinct of the politician the usefulness of men of letters as propagandists. It would doubtless be of enormous assistance to him should he ever be in a position to enforce claims to the whole of Western Europe to have the historical precedent of Arthur's conquests, so conveniently discovered by Geoffrey of Monmouth. It was no accident that two translations of Geoffrey were made within a few years. That Henry instigated the exhuming of the bodies of Arthur and Guenevere at Glastonbury is almost certain, and that he did it with the deliberate purpose of destroying the hope of Welsh, Cornish, and Bretons that Arthur would come again from his island paradise of Avalon to deliver Britain from the Saxons and Normans seems scarcely less certain.

Eleanor's attitude toward literature was not that of her husband. In the South from which she came, though troubadours were so far subject to material considerations as to be obliged frequently to rhapsodize over homely countesses and chatelaines for their bread and butter, they were not as a rule the tools of politicians. And there in the South they evolved for the first time a theory of love that was at once unconventional and yet exalted. The orthodox doctrine as it had crystallized through the Dark Ages was something like this: Woman, though created by God, had practically become the Devil's most valuable ally. She was not only inferior; she was naturally vicious. Witness the Wife of Bath: "It is an impossible that any clerk wol speke good of wyves, but-if it be of holy seintes lyves." Intercourse with

her was evil, but since it was better to marry than to
burn, each man was permitted to provide himself
with one wife. Among the most powerful the choice
was determined primarily by interest. The woman,
with almost universal approval, was forced to give
herself to the man with the sharpest sword or the
longest pedigree. If she liked him, *tant mieux*; if
she loathed him, *tant pis*. She could at least look
forward in her old age to the calm of a cloister.
Theologically woman was the Devil's decoy; polit-
ically she was a useful cement in the feudal structure.

Now in the South of France during the twelfth
century various heresies flourished. There was the
rival religion of the Albigenses, which was destined
to be abolished early in the thirteenth century by the
combined forces of the Church and Northern feudal-
ism. There was the disturbing influence of intercourse with Moors of Spain and Africa. There was
the new social creed of chivalry and courtly love,
which spread so rapidly throughout Europe that the
doctrine of the inferiority of women has never had
the same standing since. Though in conservative
congregations the woman still promises to obey her
husband, she probably hears far less than did her
ancestress of the year 1100 of the natural depravity
of Eve's daughters. What was this new social
theory which had such momentous consequences for
life and literature? In the first place, in an ecstasy
of revulsion, woman was exalted from her position
as Devil's puppet and breeding animal to a place
little below that of High God. She it was who in-

spired her lover to courtesy, to gentleness, to hardihood and great emprise. He placed himself wholly in her service, and adored her with a religious worship.

This relationship was spontaneous; no politic calculations entered into it; in fact, marriage was an irrelevant consideration. One might marry the woman one loved if circumstances were favorable, or one might love the woman one had married. But that was merely a lucky coincidence. The *mariage de convenance* was too solid a structure to demolish. So letting it alone, the lovers of Provence built themselves a fair palace of dreams apart.

This relationship was lasting and binding over all other earthly ties. Hardships must be endured, sacrifices made. Nor absence nor age nor religious differences could absolve. Love was eternal.

Now it has been objected that the theory of courtly love was not often observed in its perfection and frequently proved an excuse for a banal "free love." But if we are to judge of institutions by their perversions and of ideals by their infringements, what becomes of marriage itself? What more need be said for courtly love than that its ideals of spontaneity, of reverence for woman, have been gradually appropriated and made the ideals of marriage?

The theory of courtly love inspired Guillaume de Lorris, Petrarch, and Dante, and without it we should not have had the *Prose Lancelot,* the *Legend of Good Women,* or the *Faerie Queene.*

Among the poets whom one can afford to mention

in the same breath with these great names was one
Thomas. It is next to certain that he lived in England and wrote his romance of Tristram for the
favor of Queen Eleanor or one of her family, for his
period lies about 1185 and he ascribes to the hero of
his poem the golden lion on a red field, the first
known cognizance of the English royal house. There
is a curious group of facts connecting Eleanor with
the earliest popularization of the Tristram theme in
French and Anglo-Norman literature. Between
1150 and 1160 two troubadours intimately known
to Eleanor refer to Tristram and Ysolt as famous
lovers. Under the patronage of one of Eleanor's
daughters, Marie de Champagne, Crestien de
Troyes composed a poem, now lost, "del roi Marc
et d'Iseut la blonde." Marie de France, a lady of
Eleanor's court in London, preserves an episode of
the tradition in her *Chievrefoil*. Thomas's romance,
then, dealt with a theme already well known to
Eleanor and her circle.

Moreover, Thomas in order to support a modi-
fication of his own, cites as his authority (p. 262)
a certain Breri, "which knew the gests and the tales
of all the kings and all the earls that have been in
Britain." From other sources we learn that there
was a certain famous Welsh "fabulator," Bledhe-
ricus or Bleheris, who told tales of Arthurian themes
before a Count of Poitiers. Now that Count of
Poitiers must have been either Eleanor's father,
William VIII, or her grandfather, William VII, the
famous troubadour. All the evidence dovetails per-

fectly. Eleanor, as a romantic girl, in some painted castle-hall of Poitiers or Bordeaux must have listened more than once to the famous Welshman as he told in French the moving tale of unsanctified passion, acting it out with dramatic voice and gesture.

Whence did that story come? That in itself is a story. There is little doubt that two names have come from the Scotch Lowlands. Loonois, Tristram's homeland, is no sunken land lying west of Cornwall, but Lothian. The name of Tristram himself is derived, by common consent of scholars, from a Drust, son of Talorc, who ruled over the Picts about 780. A fragment of the Pictish saga of Drust survives in that part of the Irish *Wooing of Emer* which bears a close resemblance to the romance of Tristram. For Cuchulinn is accompanied on this series of adventures by one who bears precisely the name of Tristram's original, Drust, the adventures are placed in the Hebrides, close to Pictland; and they remind us strongly of Tristram's (pp. 60-128) : the lamentation of the people over a human tribute exacted from them, the hero's inquiry concerning the cause, his victory, his wounding, the false claimant, the recognition of the hero by a princess as he takes a bath, the offer of the princess in marriage by her father. [1] It would be entirely natural for

[1] This parallel, clearly pointed out by M. Deutschbein in 1904 (*Beiblatt zur Anglia*, XV, 16-21), has been strangely overlooked or unduly depreciated. An English translation is given by E. Hull, *Cuchullin Saga*, p. 81. Cf. Thurneysen, *Irische Helden und Königsage*, 382, 392 f.

[xx]

Irish story-tellers, transferring the story of Drust to Cuchulinn, to retain the original hero in a minor rôle. From the Picts the story of Drust, son of Talorc, passed southwards to the Welsh, who called him Drystan or Trystan map Tallwch and who celebrated his fame as a master of tricks and machines and as a lover, the lover of Esyllt, wife of March. A remnant of the old Welsh love-story is preserved in sixteenth century form, but its essential antiquity is proved both by its early version of the affair of Kaherdin and Bringvain and by its similarity to the ancient Irish legend of Diarmaid and Grainne, which, as Miss Schoepperle showed, was the source of the forest episode in the Tristram romance. Even in Thomas's version the episodes of the separating sword (pp. 180 f.) and the splashing water (pp. 226 f.) are clearly derived from the same Irish tradition as is the Welsh *Ystoria Trystan*. Since this important and amusing Welsh tale is not easily accessible, I offer here a close translation of the prose passages and a moderately faithful rendering of the verse. Those who are interested in its relation to the legend of Diarmaid and Grainne may find a satisfactory version of the latter in Joyce's *Old Celtic Romances*.

A History of Trystan

IN the meanwhile Trystan, son of Tallwch, and Esyllt, the wife of March, son of Meirchion, fled into the forest of Celyddon, and Golwg Hafddydd (Visage of a Summer's Day), her handmaid, and Bach Bychan (Little

Little), his page, brought pasties and wine with them. And
a bed of leaves was dight for them. Then March, son of
Meirchion, went unto Arthur to make plaint by reason of
Trystan, and to beseech him to avenge his injury upon him,
for that he was nigher of kin unto Arthur than was Trystan,
in that March, son of Meirchion, was cousin german to
Arthur, and Trystan was but a nephew, son of a cousin
german, to him. "I will go, I and the men of my house-
hold," said Arthur," to obtain either denial or amends for
thee." And then they surrounded the wood of Celyddon.
Trystan had certain virtues: whosoever drew blood upon
him would die; and on whomsoever he drew blood he
would die. When Esyllt heard the clamor and the voices
from every part of the wood, she trembled between the arms
of Trystan. Trystan asked her wherefore she trembled, and
she said it was because she feared for him. Then spake
Trystan:

> Feel no terror, Esyllt fair.
> While one couch with thee I share,
> Thee three hundred shall not bear
> From me, though they hauberks wear.

And then Trystan arose and took his sword in his hand
and approached the host the swiftest he might until he met
March, son of Meirchion. March, son of Meirchion, said:
"I will slay myself to slay him." But then said the other
men: "Shame be to us if we meddle with him." And then
went Trystan through the three hosts scatheless. And Kae
Hir (the Tall) loved Golwg Hafddydd, and thus he did:
he went where Esyllt was and sang this stave:

> Loving sea-gull, Esyllt fair—
> If to speak with thee I dare—
> Trystan has escaped the snare.

[xxii]

Esyllt: Noble Kae, if thou unfold
Naught but truth in what thou'st told,
Thou shalt win a maid of gold.

Kae Hir: For my tidings I require
No maid of gold or other hire;
Golwg Hafddydd I desire.

Esyllt: If the tidings I may trow
Which thy mouth has uttered, thou
Shalt have Golwg Hafddydd now.

Then March, son of Meirchion, went another time to Arthur and lamented unto him that he obtained neither denial nor atonement for his wife. "I know no counsel for thee but this," said Arthur: "to send men with instruments of music to play to him from afar, and after that to send men of song with staves of praise to praise him and to withdraw him from his wrath and anger." And this they did. Thereupon Trystan called the minstrels to him and gave them handfuls of gold and silver. After that the Chief of Peace was sent to him, to wit, Gwalchmai, son of Gwyar; and then Gwalchmai sang this ancient rime:

Fierce is the unbounded wave
When the middle sea doth rave.
Who art thou, O warrior brave?

Trystan: Fierce are thunder and the flame,
Though they be no whit the same.
In battle Trystan is my name.

Gwalchmai: Trystan, I can nowhere see
Blemish in thy chivalry.
Gwalchmai once was friend to thee.

Trystan: If Gwalchmai in the day of blood
Needed me, for him I would
Do more than a brother could.

Introduction

Gwalchmai:	Trystan, noble prince of light,
	Sore thy buffets. I am hight
	Gwalchmai, Arthur's nephew wight.
Trystan:	When, O Gwalchmai, I should see
	Battle's burden weary thee,
	I would shed blood to the knee.
Gwalchmai:	Trystan with the heart of fire,
	Thou wouldst give all I require;
	I would do thy least desire.
Trystan:	This I ask to shield my head;
	This I ask not out of ᷄ ᷄
	Whose this band against me ᷄᷄
Gwalchmai:	Trystan, worthily renowned,
	Dost thou know not, hast not found,
	Arthur's host that hems thee round?
Trystan:	Arthur I fear not a whit;
	Nine hundred fights give proof of it.
	I will smite if I am smit.
Gwalchmai:	Trystan, friend of maids, before
	Thou begin the deeds of gore,
	Better far is peace than war.
Trystan:	If my sword is at my thigh,
	And my right hand wakeful, I
	Envy not my enemy.
Gwalchmai:	Trystan, thy repute is clear,
	And thy blow can cleave a spear.
	Spurn not Arthur's friendship dear.
Trystan:	Gwalchmai of the gracious deeds,
	Rain may drench a hundred meads.
	Arthur's love in me love breeds.

Introduction

Gwalchmai: Trystan, men thy praise rehearse;
               A hundred oaks rain may immerse.
               Come and with thy friend converse.

Trystan: Stubborn Gwalchmai, this I know:
               A hundred fields rain may o'erflow.
               Where thou willest I will go.

Then went Trystan and Gwalchmai unto Arthur, and Gwalchmai sang this stave:

               Arthur, rich in courtesies,
               Rain may drench a hundred trees.
               Here is Trystan; be at ease.

Arthur: Gwalchmai, man of worth complete,
               From fight thou soughtest not retreat.
               I my nephew Trystan greet.

Trystan said nothing in spite of that, and Arthur sang another stave.

               Trystan, prince of warrior horde,
               The love thou dost thyself accord
               Give thy kin and me, their lord.

Trystan said nothing in spite of that, and Arthur sang the third stave.

               Trystan, war-prince, take from me
               A champion's share of gift and fee:
               Give me love and loyalty.

In spite of that, Trystan said nothing.

Arthur: Trystan, very wise thou art;
               Hold thy kinsmen in thy heart;
               Coldness doth not kinsmen part.

Then Trystan answered Arthur:
>   Arthur, I have heeded well.
>   First to thee my mind I'll tell:
>   'Gainst thy will I'll ne'er rebel.

Then Arthur made peace between Trystan and March, son of Meirchion, and Arthur spake with them both in turn; and neither of them consented to be without Esyllt. Then Arthur judged her to the one while the leaves were on the wood, and to the other while the leaves were not on the wood, and to her husband to make the choice. He chose the time when the leaves were not on the wood, because at that season the nights would be longer. Arthur announced that unto Esyllt, and she said: "Blessed is the judgment and he who gave it"; and sang this stave:

>   Three trees have a happy way:
>   Holly, ivy, yew, are they;
>   Green they keep their leaves alway.
>   Trystan's am I then for aye.

In this wise March, son of Meirchion, lost his wife for ever. Thus ends the history.

It seems clear, then, that the Welsh established the relationship and the names of the famous triangle, connected the story loosely with the Arthurian cycle, introduced Kae Hir (alias Sir Kay and Kaherdin) as the friend of the hero, and told of his affair with Esyllt's maid (pp. 239 f.), and made much of the flight of the lovers to the forest (pp. 177-79). The legend of Trystan must have undergone further elaboration in Celtic territory, for as related by Thomas it contains a number of other Celtic traits: the rudderless voyage (pp. 80-83), the sub-

[xxvi]

stitution in the bridal bed and the attempt on
Bringvain's life (pp. 134-36), the harp and the
rote (pp. 140-45), the floating chips used as
a signal (p. 155), the spying dwarf (pp. 155 f., 158,
182), Petit Cru (pp. 169 f.), the secret visits to a
mistress in a subterranean chamber (p. 221). The
great popularity of the central theme has obviously
inspired many a Welsh and Cornish raconteur to add
from the storehouse of Celtic lore new tests, new
triumphs, for the lovers.

It is to the Cornish raconteurs, of course, that we
owe the immortalization of Tintagel—Tintagel with
its shattered walls, its chasm and cliffs, its high, green
headland, and its quiet cove, the perfect setting for
imperishable romance. One French version, moreover, localizes Mark's court at Lantien. The legend,
like the other Arthurian romances, then passed over
to Brittany and was popularized there by the year
1000. A certain Breton lord, Rivalon by name,
happened to christen his son Tristan, and so it came
about that when the Breton *conteurs* were inventing
antecedents for the legendary hero, they named his
father after the Breton Rivalon rather than after
the Welsh Tallwch. Indeed the account of Tristram's parentage, birth, and boyhood seem to have
been created where they are localized,—in Brittany.

What of the great tragic ending? Is that, too,
as Breton in its origin as in its setting It seems
probable. But it is certain that the momentous con-
ception of a second Ysolt, Ysolt of Brittany, is derived, through whatever channels, from Arabic

romance. The kernel is clearly discoverable in the tale of the loves of Kais and Lobna, of which the following is a summary:

A young man, Kais by name, fell deeply in love with and married a woman named Lobna. The marriage was childless, and after ten years of pressure from his father Kais allowed Lobna to depart. He fell ill and proclaimed to his physician that he and Lobna had been destined for each other before the creation, and that the grave would not end their love. Finally, once more his father's will prevailed and he went to seek another wife. When a maiden told him that her name was Lobna, he fell in a swoon. Her brother sought his friendship and after several weeks brought about the marriage of his sister and Kais. But Kais would neither approach nor speak to his new wife, but continued to communicate, through messengers, with the first Lobna, who had meanwhile been married by force to a second husband. Kais complained of her indifference, but she came to him by night and justified herself. Naturally the family of the second Lobna were not pleased. The versions differ as to whether Kais or his love Lobna died first, but one represents him as mourning over Lobna's grave, declaring that her death is his death, and relates that both the lovers were buried in one grave.

From the Orient, too, came certain tales of successful deception such as the tryst under the tree (p. 157) and the ambiguous oath (pp. 163–68).

It seems impossible to decide whether some anonymous Breton *conteur* first wove these strands of Oriental silk into the embroidery of Celtic design, or whether it was Bleheris himself. The background for the second Ysolt theme is of course Brittany, but the Midi would be a more probable point of contact with Oriental story. At any rate, the blended tale which Bleheris told to the count of Poitiers perfectly exemplified the creed of courtly love. For Ysolt, as for Grainne, the claims of her husband were as naught beside the claims of love. For Tristram, as for Kais, the claims of his wife were as naught beside the claims of love. The Celtic and the Arabic tales had come from the West and the East to unite and form a harmonious whole, embodying the new French creed of love and destined to be heard wherever the French tongue was known. The superb finale was further enriched by far-off echoes from old Greek romance—from the death of Aegeus and the death of Paris.

The precise version which Bleheris made famous by his passionate recital was not, so far as we know, written down. There is no such close resemblance in incident and phrase between Béroul, Thomas, and Eilhart as would surely exist if they followed a single poem in manuscript form. What we have, probably, is a number of written versions following the main lines of Bleheris' story, but subjected to the changes of successive oral reciters and to the influence of earlier forms. The Norman Béroul had the eye of a painter and tells his tale with verve and color. Thomas is distinguished by his rationalizing tendency and his remarkable interest in character. He makes an eloquent appeal to reason to justify his account as against less sensible variants. He seems to have decided in the face of tradition to sever the association of Tristram with Arthur and to assign them to different periods. He abolishes the delightful episode of the swallow bearing the golden hair and the quixotic search for the princess to whom the hair belonged, and substituted a purposeful mission to win a known maiden. He suppresses the revolting scene where Mark delivers Ysolt to lepers. He insists not only upon the courtly accomplishments of his hero and heroine but also upon their learning. Though he must have belonged to the clergy himself, there is no puritanical complex in his handling of words and situations. Nor is there the slighest indication that his clerical calling required him to minimize the depth, faith, and endurance of this unhallowed love.

There are incoherences and improbabilities in the narrative. Moreover, it is hard to understand why Thomas did not suppress the barbaric episode of Ysolt's attempted procurement of Bringvain's death; and why he permitted his hero more than once to leave Ysolt to the savage vengeance of Mark. But there are also passages of unusual psychological insight: the fury of Bringvain at the taunts of Cariadoc, the explosion of epithets and threats with which she works off the smart of her humiliation upon Ysolt, and the deep-lying devotion to Ysolt and Tristram, which prompts the clever lie by which she shields them even more completely than before from Mark's suspicions. And though Thomas drags out soliloquy and dialog sometimes to a tedious length, after the fashion set by Ovid and imitated by

Introduction

courtly romancers, it is not through lack of feeling. His handling of Tristram's torment on the night of his wedding to Ysolt of Brittany is no mere perfunctory demonstration of true love's supremacy over carnal desire and conjugal obligations. It is a faithful psychological record of the ebb and flow of passion after passion. More than that, Thomas himself rises and sinks, rises and sinks, in those tempestuous seas, and the billows of agony break over his head. And he loses all prolixity in the swift and direct culmination of the romance. Ysolt hastening up the steep street, lifting her long gown before her, the wonder of the people, the tolling of the bells, the last despairing words over Tristram's body, and Thomas's own epilog—these are all in the great tradition of medieval, yes, of universal literature.

That the poem of Thomas was appreciated at the English court is to be inferred not only from its intrinsic worth, but also from some curious pieces of evidence. In the reign of King John there was among the regalia "a sword of Tristram." This sword, of course, would have had a piece broken out. And though in the reign of John's successor, Henry III, it no longer is mentioned as Tristram's sword, it appears in the records as Curtana, the short sword. A replica of Curtana, made at the Restoration of the Stuarts after the destruction of the original during the Commonwealth, showed plainly the splintered edge where the point had been broken off. The present Curtana, still carried in the Coronation ceremony, preserves in the shortened blade a reminder of royal interest in Tristram's legend.

Though Henry III evidently lost the tradition of the hero's sword, he did not lose the hero's story as told by Thomas. It has been plausibly suggested that this king commissioned the very fine set of pavement tiles which have been and may yet be dug up on the site of Chertsey Abbey. These were designed about 1270, and fill out for us many of the scenes of adventure nearly as they were imagined by Thomas himself. It must have troubled the contemplations of many a tonsured Benedictine to discover at his feet these charming reminders of the adventurous and stirring life to be lived outside the abbey walls. It is indeed a fortunate circumstance that they have been preserved to furnish illustrations for the romance.

But the influence of Thomas was felt not only by kings and craftsmen. It was naturally felt most deeply by men of his own calling. About 1300 a very much garbled and condensed version in a jingling meter was made in English under the title of *Sir Tristrem*. In 1226 a certain Brother Robert made for King Haakon of Norway, that enthusiast for Anglo-Norman culture and the friend of Henry III, a Norse saga of Tristram and Isond. This saga furnishes in considerable measure a word-for-word translation of Thomas. The passages of psychological analysis are unfortunately cut or condensed, and the almost cursory treatment of the potion scene is unpardonable. Nevertheless, except for one short

Introduction

passage, Robert gives so faithful a rendering of the general content of his original that, barring that passage, I have used the saga to supply the lost portions of Thomas, and have followed it, except for the first fifteen chapters, which I condense, with almost verbal exactness. Footnotes indicate which parts of the present reconstruction follow the Norse, which parts follow the original French, and which passage has been reconstructed from other evidence.

But Thomas inspired others besides tyros and mere translators. From him derives the *Tristan* of Gottfried von Strassburg, which many critics consider, next to the *Divina Commedia* and the *Canterbury Tales*, the greatest narrative poem of the Middle Ages. Through Gottfried the influence reached Wagner, and through *Sir Tristrem*, Swinburne; filtered through various media, it reached Matthew Arnold and E. A. Robinson. In the reading of Thomas of Britain, then, one sees not only such a quaintly carved laver of marble as decked many a medieval pleasaunce, and such a seething and swirling of clear waters welling up tumultuously from caverns deep in the hills, but also the fountainhead of great rivers that have made glad the gorges and the valleys of romance.

THE ROMANCE OF
TRISTRAM AND YSOLT

THE ROMANCE OF TRISTRAM AND YSOLT

Chapter i

IN Brittany was a youth, right fair of his body, free of his bounty, mighty in castles and holds, cunning in many arts, wise of counsel, a strong man of his hands, and in all things he passed the men of that land, and his name was called Rivalon. He had about him so great a company of knights and lords that his store might not sustain them. Yet by his prowess and his forays he won so many lands from his foes that his worship increased and his goods. In the third year sithen he first bare arms, he gathered an host and warred on many a king and duke, and wrought them much loss, burning the King's castles and towns, so that many of his knights yielded themselves prisoner, and from them he took great ransoms, gold and silver, horses and raiment. At the last, the King by the assent of his wisest men was accorded and met with him to make a covenant. When the covenant was made, Rivalon gave his realm into the governance of a warden, and he let ordain a company to go forth into other countries, to prove himself and to win worship and to show his

prowess. Much did men say concerning England,
that it was peaceful and rich, with great store of
gentle knights and great castles and the richest hunting grounds of beasts and fowl, and well furnished
with gold and silver, robes and horses, gris and
sable and white bear's skin. Therefore, he desired
to see their customs and their nobleness, and to
prove their puissance.

Chapter ii

SO with a score men, well conditioned and
hardy, well furnished with arms and horses, he
passed the sea and landed in Cornwall. Now was
King Mark king over all men in England, and he
lay in the town of Tintagel, where was the most
strongest castle in all the realm. And Rivalon drew
unto Tintagel, and whenas he came into the court,
he alight off his horse, and his fellows likewise, and
they passed into the hall, clad in rich clothes, heeding
courteous custom, going together two and two, and
each held other by the hand. When Rivalon and
his fellows came before the King, each saluted other
right seemly. When the King had heard their
speech, he bade Rivalon sit beside him, but his fellows he let sit further from him, as is the manner of
courts. And the King asked him of tidings, and
he told him peaceful and blithe tidings, and said
whence and for what cause he was come, that he
might sojourn with him and his worshipful fellow-

ship, to have pleasaunce and to learn gentle taches. Then King Mark received him with honor and all his fellows, and set them above his own knights.

Chapter iii

WHEN Rivalon had tarried a certain time with the King in all honor and worship, Mark ordained a great feast, and he sent sealed letters hither and thither over the land, and bade all the earls, dukes, and barons with their wives, sons, and daughters. When all had heard the bidding of the King, they gave heed and made ready their journey. So came all the worthiest men of the realm and lords of all the isles around, and assembled them in Cornwall in a forest nigh to a lake. There were fair meadows and wide, smooth and dight with fair grasses and flowers in plenty; and for that this was a place right pleasant, Mark let pitch here large pavilions, yellow and green, blue and red and richly adorned, gilt and embroidered with gold, under the sweet smelling leaves and fresh blossoms. There the new-dubbed knights and bachelors jousted without malice or falseness, and won the love of fair damozels and gentle ladies that were comen with their husbands and lovers to the feast.

Chapter iv

WHEN now Mark beheld all this goodly chivalry, his joy increased, thinking that he was whole lord of so rich a land and so courteous men and women. And he bethought him how he might order this entertainment that never none might pass it, and he showed all his folk and men of worship much honor with a feast of costly meats. When the King and all had eaten their fill, the younger men went forth to the fields to try their strengths, and the squires brought them their horses and arms. And when they were armed they leapt on their horses running and jousted right eagerly for the love of ladies and for to show who wrought most knightly. And Rivalon was above all most valiant and best bare his arms and won most worship, for all that assembly of damozels and ladies set their eyes on him and desired him albeit they had never tofore seen him nor knew not whence he was nor his condition nor name. For such is the nature of women to desire out of measure and to crave that they cannot possess and to despise that they have, right as it befell with Dido, who loved so wildly that she brent herself when her lover that was come from another land departed from her.

Chapter v

THIS King Mark had one sister that was so fair
to see and courteous, kind and worshipful that
such a rose was not in the world known of men. Her
deeds witnessed to all in that realm that there was
none her peer of wisdom and courtesy, largess and
bravery, so that mighty and weak, young and old,
rich and poor praised her, and so widely men asked
concerning her in other realms that her fame waxed,
and great love arose in great princes and fair seeming
youths or ever they beheld her.

Chapter vi

BUT although this gentle maid increased in good
conditions and fortunes, yet it happed with her
as oft is said that seldom is there thing that lacketh
naught. For forthwithal when she saw this man,
she endured such manifold torments of mind that
she misdoubted wherein she might have offended
against God that so heavy a fate should befall her,
albeit never by word or deed did she wrong no man,
but rather gave ease and pleasure. Right piteous
was the case of this noble damozel when she went
forth from her pavilion in rich apparel and with her
a company of fair maidens to behold the joustings.
When she had regarded a while the sport, she
happed of a sudden to espy Rivalon, that excelled

all other of prowess and knighthood, and right so there fell on her sore yearning and she sighed from her heart. She was torn all inwardly and burned, and she knew sorrow but not whence it came. Anon she sighed again, and waxed all pale, and was nigh wood for the burning that had seized her.

"O Lord God," quoth she, "whence cometh on me this marvelous malady? No pain have I in my limbs, but this burning burneth me, I wot not how. I am out of my wit therewith that I may not endure it, yet meseemeth I am whole. Is there no leech that may give me a healing draught? Certes the heat of the sun hath not so envenomed me. Never tofore might I believe that I should endure such frenzy that burning maketh me to shiver and cold to sweat. These twain, heat and cold, are so intermeddled that neither may be severed from other, and for that I must needs endure both, for none will bring me heal."

Thus the gentle damozel Blanchefleur was long rent of divers torments.

Chapter vii

THEREWITHAL she looked down and was ware how the knights rode their horses fairly across the fields, and how they brake the stoutest spears upon their shields in their stiff jousting. Then her burning abated at sight of that fair place, and the sport did somewhat comfort and rejoice her: for it is the wont of love that when one is frenzied for love, if he work not but repair him to some resort of delight, then is love much lighter to endure. So was it with this young maid. But it was not long ere Rivalon proved himself mightier than the rest and bare himself more fairly, and her anguish was renewed many fold.

"Certes," saith she, "this man is full of sorceries that I am tormented so sorely by so short a sight of him. God, be thou my shield, for great trouble ariseth of these knights, and certes, if all that behold him know such pains as I, he hath indeed subtle crafts and evil poisons to corrupt men, for at sight of him I quake and burn all over. Alas, Lord, how may this woe and anguish be taken from me? For rather it beseemeth him to beg than me to proffer this thing, and so should I shame me and my kin: and he would deem me of them that lightly change their loves, and hold me in scorn. But wherefore should I complain me of these matters; for none other wise may I utter them; and it betideth with me as with many another, that I choose but what I must."

Chapter viii

WHEN the knights had ridden as long as them liked, they rode from the fields, and Rivalon, the courteous, came thereas the fair Blanchefleur abode with her damozels, and he greeted her with fair words:

[7]

"God thee bless, fair lady."

And she anon with blithe semblaunt answered: "If, as thou art a good knight, thou amend that wherein thou hast wronged me, then mayest thou be honored and blessed."

When Rivalon heard that word, he bethought him thereon, and said: "Gentle maiden, what be these matters wherein I have thee wronged?"

Blanchefleur said: "I trow that thou alone of these men knowest not that thou hast mischiefed me in certain matters, and I am thereof right wroth." And she called him to her, for well she wist that she was constrained thereto.

And he answered her with honorable words: "Right fair damozel, by God's will, I will demean me by thee worthily and with worship, and thou shalt be judge thereof."

Blanchefleur said: "By no mean will I release thee from my reproach ere I see whether thou wilt do me amends."

When they had spoken thus, Rivalon gave her good day and rode forth, and the damozel sighed and said: "God in heaven keep thee."

Now rideth Rivalon studying what that might be that the King's sister said he had misdone by her and that she would have him amend. He thought on her sigh, yet the more he mused, the less did he understand that she meant. All that day was he troubled with thought, neither by night as he lay in his bed could he find no rest.

Chapter ix

NOW they endure both a single woe, and great is their distress and wilderment: she loveth him with her whole heart, and he her with a steadfast mind, yet neither was ware of other's pain. Sithen he was wise and courteous, he cast how he might have speech with her. In this as in all else he did honorably, for a great hindrance lay tofore them: if King Mark wist that so young a knight and but new-come to his court had cast his fantasy and desire on a woman of so high lineage and so nigh of his own blood, then might he no wise attain to his desire.

Chapter x

WHAT need we speak hereof more, for all that have reason know well that it is the wont of lovers to accomplish their strong loves as soon as ever they may by coming together in privity. So did these twain all their will, and for none had suspicion at their meetings, they held their fellowship without slander or blame. The King wist naught thereof nor none in his court, and men marveled for what cause Rivalon dwelt so long there. At the last it was told to King Mark that Rivalon had great liking unto his sister, and that he would fain ask her of him and wed her with his counsel and consent.

[9]

And the King, for that Rivalon surmounted all other in all conditions that long to noble men, thought to espouse them with a great feast, and for this cause he suffered them freely to converse together as it liked them.

Chapter xi

LONG it was not after that the King fared with a noble meynie to a tourney, and when they were come thither, they ordained their joustings and made disport with great fierceness. Now arose the stiffest debate out of measure, so that from naught they withheld them, and on both parties they took life. Then the valiant Rivalon dashed like a beast fearless into the medley, wounded and slew many strong knights, and made great slaughter. Forthwith as he pressed against them that would withstand him, he was wounded with a grievous wound and nigh smitten through with a sword, that he fell from his horse as he were dead. And the play ended not ere many noble knights were wounded or slain or captived. His fellows took Rivalon and bare him home half dead: and now arose great sorrow and dole of all his company. Whenas the King's sister wist the heavy plight of her lover, then was her grief the greater that it was hidden in her breast, and that she had great dread of her brother, the King, and the other mighty men. Therefore she wept in great anguish alone.

Chapter xii

THUS were set this gentle lady and her valiant lover in sore distress, and she supposed that if he should die and she might not come nigh him, never might she have solace. So she yode unto her foster-mother and discovered to her her sorrow, and bade follow her. And she went with such cunning and subtlety that none was ware thereof save her foster-mother and such as she would, and she came unto her lover when the chamber was voided, and all departed thence. When she beheld him, she fell distract upon his bed, and rehearsed her woe and dolor. And when she had somewhat recovered her, she clipped him and kissed him oft, saying, "Sweetest love," and the tears wetting her face. And he in all his pain and anguish embraced her with such hot desire that this noble damozel conceived. She in grief and he in pain, they there begat a child, the which in his life thereafter brought woe to all his friends; and of him is this history made.

Chapter xiii

NOW when they ceased their game and speech, she yode unto her bower. And he let purvey a passing wise leech, and he healed his wound as it was tofore. Then came a messenger from his realm and brought tidings from his kinsmen and vassals

[11]

that the Bretons harried his land, slew his folk, and brent his towns. When he heard that, it seemed him he might no longer dwell there, and with all speed he made ready his horses and ships and arms and other gear for the journey. When his lady heard thereof, then waxed her misery, and when he came to take leave of her unto his return, she said thus:

"Wit ye well, such a lover am I that I love thee with a longing that will not be denied, for I must surely die but if God have mercy on me. For after thy departing may I never have mirth nor comfort. It repenteth me of my love, for meseemeth it leadeth to greater woes. And of two woes I wot not which I would choose; for I am heavy for thy departing, yet am I in dread for thee, shouldst thou tarry here. If I were not with child of thee, then should I more lightly abide after and more quietly bear my sorrow. But now if thou leavest me, it grieveth me that ever I beheld thee. Yet liefer would I die alone than mischief come upon us both, for thou deservest not to die. Sooner beseemeth me to die for thy sake than that thou, my love, were slain guiltless. Wherefore it rejoiceth me of thy going that thou mayest not die abiding here: then were our child fatherless and of thee might not learn honor and worship. Woe is me to look on thy knowledge and courtesy and knightly valiance! Alas, I have betrayed me and I am lost and perished."

Then fell she in a swoon into his embrace. And

RIVALON RECEIVETH A MESSENGER

thereafter she came to herself, weeping and lamenting, and he solaced her and set her beside him, and dried her eyes and face, and said:

"Fair love, I will do in this matter as I best may and as most behoveth us both. I knew not the thing thou hast told me, but now syne that I know, I will do that is most seemly, so that either I shall abide with thee, though there be peril therein, or thou wilt follow me to mine own land, and there will I do thee all the honor that longeth to our love. Now choose thou as thee list."

Chapter xiv

WHEN she understood his intent and that her will was his will, would she then nothing blame him, and she said right heartily:

"My friend and love, here may we not tarry with freedom: wit ye well that if we abide, we abide in woe and jeopardy."

And so took they counsel how she might go with him unto his land. Then Rivalon took leave of the King, and hied him to the ships with Blanchefleur and found there his men all ready. Then they raised the mast, hoisted sail, and had a fair wind, so that they came hale and sound, and landed anon in Brittany. When he was come to his realm, he found his men hard bestead by their enemies: and he summoned his liegemen and councillors, and told them all that was fallen and of his love.

Then took he Blanchefleur in lawful wedlock and with rightwise sacraments, and held high feast. Then he sent her secretly to a mighty and strong castle; and there he let keep her in seemly wise for a space.

Chapter xv

O N a day Rivalon armed him and rode unto battle to win the towns and castles of his realm, and there lacked not many sad strokes, and many shields to-shivered, and wounds and death on both parties, and many lords and knights were taken prisoner. In this battle was Rivalon, the courteous knight, shot through the body, and he fell from his horse dead to the earth. And all his men grieved sore, and bare his body home to the castle. Then was groaning and weeping, and they took thought for naught save it were to inter him in the earth honorably. But his noble lady took such sorrow that none might comfort her. She swooned oft, and lay as dead, and groaned in sore distress, refusing all solace. Death is her delight and gladness only: liefer would she die than live, saying:

"Unhappy am I above all ladies. Wherefore should I live after so renowned a knight? I was his life and solace, and he my love and life. Whereof should I take comfort when my delight is in his grave? It behoveth us die both together. And sithen Death may not come to me, I must go to meet Death that knocketh at my heart. My life shall follow his life. An I were delivered of this child, I would fain go unto my death."

When she had thus made her moan, she fell in a swoon on her bed, and her womb began to travail. Now hath she sorrow and pain both, and she was in these throes until the third day, and in the night after the third day, she brought forth a fair boy with great travail and weakness, and when the child was born, she gave up her breath. Now was the woe of their barons increased, and some wept for their lord, and other for their lady, and all made dolorous cheer for them both. Sorrow was there in the hall among the barons for the departing of their lord, but more was the sorrow in the chamber among the gentlewomen for the death of their lady. And all wept that saw the boy so young, and withal fatherless and motherless.

Chapter xvi

WHEN now the Seneschal wist the evil fortune of his fair lady, he said that the child should be christened that he might not die unchristened: and then came a priest with a chrism, and gave it to the child, and said what name he should bear.

"Methinketh wise," said he, "that for the sake of the woe and anguish, grief and dole, sorrow and malease, wounds and pains, and of the miserable fortune that befell us of his birth, the boy be called Tristram." In this word "trist" meaneth "sad," and "hum" meaneth "man"; and his name was changed for that fairer is Tristram spoken than Trist-hum.

"So shall he be named," said the Seneschal, "for cause that he was born to us in woe: he hath lost his joy and solace, his father, our lord, and his mother, our lady, and it behoveth us to lament, sith he was born to us in woe and anguish."

Then was he cleped Tristram and christened with that name; and for this reason gat he that name that he was begotten in sorrow and malady, born and brought forth with grimly pains, and dolorous was all his life. Of right was he cleped Tristram, for that woeful he waked, and woeful he slept, and woeful he died, as they may come to hear that hearken further this history.

Then the Seneschal caused the bailiff bear the child from the castle secretly to his house, and let keep him honorably and privily because of his foes, and he spake to no man of the child that he was the son of his lord. But he commanded his wife to go to bed, and when some time was passed, he let her be churched, and let proclaim on every side that she had conceived and borne a child at that time, for he would not that the King of Brittany should know that this was the son of his lord. If the King were possessed of the truth, then would he slay him straight, that he might not by him suffer strife and harm, slaughter and peril to his realm. Therefore the Seneschal let nourish the boy in secret, and bred him up as his son. and fostered him in all easy conditions.

Chapter xvii

HERE may ye learn of fearless deeds and kindness and courteous conditions, for this true and faithful man was thereto wise and of good will, and made his lord his son for to defend him from danger and defend him against enemies, and honor him with worship. Then he made him to learn bookknowledge, and he was passing witty, and he perfected himself by this study in the VII chief arts, and he was cunning in all manner of tongues. Then learned he the VII kinds of music so that there was none had more renown nor more skill. And of meekness and mercy and gentle taches, in wisdom and counsel and prowess he was found peerless: of his conditions and his fame was none his pareil, so waxed he ever stronger. And when his fosterfather saw his countenance, he bestowed upon him the richest raiment, goodly horses, and all manner of hunting gear, and all the wealth that he gat he bestowed on him with princely largess and worship; so were his sons wroth and marveled for why their father loved him so much, and did him honor above his sons, with love and manifold honor, with service and marvelous kindness: therefore were they wroth with their father for that they thought Tristram to be their brother.

Chapter xviii

IT fortuned upon a day that a great ship came sailing and cast an anchor in the haven under the castle. They were merchants of Norway, that were driven thither by long northern tempests: in their ship was much gris and white fur, skin of beaver and bear-fell and sable, walrus ivory and wax, goshawks and gray falcons and white, hides and goat skins, dried fish and tar, oil and brimstone, and all manner wares of Norway. Tidings hereof came to the castle, and the sons of the Seneschal said and called to them Tristram.

"What shall we do," said they, "that have no falcons to delight us? Now be comen here in the ship many birds and right fair. If thou wilt help us, thou mayest compass all thou wilt require of our father, for never doth he nor our mother withsay naught thou askest. Rather will they buy VII of the fairest than to see thee in distress."

They besought him so sore that he assented unto them, and they all hied them to the ship, and Tristram let show the birds. The merchants were of Norway and could neither Breton nor French nor other tongues to make their chaffer. Now Tristram was cunning in many tongues, and made a bargain with them for VII birds, and his foster-father paid the dispense thereof, and he gave them to his brothers. Then espied he there a chess-board,

TRISTRAM PLAYETH CHESS WITH THE NORSEMEN

and asked if none of the merchants would play with him, and one of them came forth, and they set the stakes and laid a great sum. When his foster-father saw that he sat at the chess-board, he said:

"My son, I go home, but thy master shall abide thee, and return with thee when thou art ready."

And there tarried with him his governor, a courteous knight and well conditioned. But the merchants had marvel of the young man and praised his knowledge and meekness and beauty and subtlety, for he overcame them all, and them seemed that if they carried him away, much profit would they have because of his knowledge and many crafts, and thereto if they wished to sell him, they would get a good price by him. So as he sat heeding the game, with all the secrecy they might they drew up the cable and anchor, and let the ship ride out from the bay. Now the ship was covered with a pavilion, and drifted with the winds and waves so that Tristram was not ware ere they were far from land. Then cried he to the merchants:

"Sirs, wherefore will ye do so?"

"Because," said they, "we will that thou follow us."

Then he began to weep and make evil cheer and to make great moan, and the knight in like wise for love of him. And the men of Norway took his governor and set him in a boat and gave him one oar and left him. The sail is now raised and the ship rideth fast, and Tristram is in their power, sorrowful and heavy. His master came to land

[23]

with sore toil and travail; little might he choose his haven or landing.

Tristram sitteth now in woe and anguish, and prayeth God to pardon him, to watch and ward him from jeopardy and hardships, that neither weapon nor wind, treason nor falsehood of these paynims do him hurt, nor he be sold into their power. He sigheth much and maketh dolorous lament.

Now is his governor come home to the castle and telleth tidings whereof none hath joy: that great multitude, a thousand men, taketh woe and heaviness of these tidings of Tristram's loss. When these tidings are told, the whole court maketh dole, and all haste them down to the strand. His foster-father passeth all other in his woe, and feeleth sorest anguish, weepeth and bemoaneth this malfortune, and calleth it all his misadventure that this hap should come upon him and this woe by evil chance befall him. And he looketh out to the sea, and crieth with a high voice:

"Tristram, my solace and my lord, my repose, my beloved and my darling, to God I thee commend, and under His ward I hide thee. Now that I have lost thee, no solace have I more in my life days, sith that we are dissevered each from other."

So dolorously ever and anon he made his plaint, and sorrowed for Tristram: and all, young and old, that were there wept and prayed for him; all they that had delight of him and were glad of him, were now full of woe and misery; rich and poor, all that knew him in all the realm, were heavy for him.

Chapter xix

NOW the Seneschal let purvey a ship in all haste with all manner of tackle and provision enow, for that he was purposed to follow the merchants and never to return on live ere it was proved for sooth where Tristram, his fosterson, was become. He made hasten all things; the ship was ready with all tackle, wine and victual. Then he yode to the board and let draw up all cables and anchors, and they hoisted sail, and sailed out of the haven, and they held now to Norway ward, and they endured toil and tossing, hunger and want, terror and misery in strange seas. They came withal to Denmark and Gothland and Iceland and Orkney and Shetland, and sought for their lord Tristram, and found him not. For when they that had carried him away were well nigh arrived in their own land, there came a sharp wind into their sail with such tempest and tide that they had been lost had they not hastily let drop the sail. The whole sea was stirred with grievous waves, it hailed and rained, and thundered and lightened: the mast was high and the sea deep, and the ship rolled for the storm so that none might stand on foot, and they let the ship drive before the wind. All moaned and feared, wept and cried wildly so that even those that of their company were hardiest waxed heavy, and all weened that they must perish, for that the wind drave them passing hard. A sennight the tempest smote and drave them that they saw no land, and even when the wind abated they had as much fear and distress, for they wist not how they might win to any land or haven. Then said they all unto the captain:

"All this storm and peril and labor that we have endured befell us of our own desert, for that we have sinned concerning Tristram in so much that we reft him from his kin and friends and land. This storm will never stint nor shall we come to land so long time as we have him on this ship. Now if God will pardon us and grant us fair wind, so that we may come to land, then promise we that as for us he shall go free."

And they all assented thereunto with a sure handfast. Forthwith the darkness passed away, and the sun shone and the tempest was ceased. Then right gladly they drew up the sail, and when they had sailed a space, they beheld land, and with all sail they made a fair course to land, and cast anchor nigh thereto. Then they suffered Tristram to go to shore, and gave him a little of their provision, and bade God give him good day. They knew not what was the land whereon they had set him, and therewith they drew up sail and went their ways.

Chapter xx

NOW is Tristram in an unknown land, hapless and helpless. He sat him down and looked after the ship that was departing, and would not go thence while that he might behold it. When it was vanished from sight, he looked about him and said with doleful cheer:

"Almighty God, that with Thy power shapest men after Thy mind, as Thou art one God in three Persons, and three Persons in one God, heed Thou me and guide me and keep me, helpless and friendless, in my peril and distress. Thou knowest whereof I have need, for I wot not whither I am become nor in what country I am set. Lo, I am here on a coast of a strange land: naught may I behold hence save fells and forests, steep cliffs and crags; nowise may I ascend from hence, nor no man may I see. I know not whether I shall escape, nor whether this country be Christian and habited of men. Here all is to me unknown save my defenceless plight. I find no man that may do me succor nor heed, nor paths nor other guides. Perchance it may be that I wot not the speech of these men, if men there be. I dread me that lions may rend me or bears bite or other savage beast that feareth not the voice of man. Ah my father, that art lost, Ah my mother, that for me weepest, Ah friends, that lament for me, Ah kinsmen that are sundered from me! Woe be to the hawks that I was so fain to buy! Woe be to the chess-board whereat I proved my skill! For their sake am I now cause of sorrow unto my friends: if they wist that I were on live, then were they glad of my life. I wot well that it availeth not to mourn therefor: what availeth it here to sit? Better is it to go forth while

the day sufficeth and I may yet see to guide my feet
if per adventure I may find an house, and win me
harborage in my trouble."

Right so he ascended a rock and found there
divers trodden paths, and one of them pursued he
with joy out of the forest. He was then sore
wearied and walked with all the haste that he might.
He was appareled richly and was big and well-
made of his body, and for the heat was great, he
went without mantle, bearing it on his shoulder.
Often he bethought him of his kin and friends, pray-
ing God to have mercy on him, and his heart was
full of sorrow. Forthwithal he saw two pilgrims
that took the same road: they were of Venice born,
and were come from St. Michael's Mount, whither
they had gone to offer their orisons. When they
perceived the youth, then was he right glad of them
and they of him.

"Friend," say they, "what man are ye, what do
ye, and whence come ye?"

Tristram wist not that they were not of that land,
and he answered craftily that they might not deem
surely in what wise he came thither walking.
"Friends," said he, "of this country am I, and seek
my fellows and find them not. We were this day
on hunting, and they followed the beasts, but I was
left here alone. They must soon return hereby, for
this way came we from home. Now tell me whither
ye are bent, and where ye cast now to abide, and
it is my will to follow you."

They answered: "In Tintagel we think to find harborage."

Then saith Tristram: "There also have I an errand, and there shall we have succor from faithful friends. When we be come thither this eve, we shall by God's will find strong friends and good hostel, and they will show us kindness sufficient."

Chapter xxi

NOW they set forth all together, Tristram and his fellows. He speereth now tidings of other lands and what was befallen among kings and princes and earls. And as they were telling him tidings, there leapt past an hart, and there followed him a great pack of hounds, grayhounds and slothounds. Some bayed, others gaped, and all chased him eagerly. The hart saw it might not avail him to run further, and he turned him into the road before the pilgrims, and then ran away to a river, and followed the course thereof, and sought a path, but the hounds were upon him, and he straightway turned him to the stream again. When at the last he came to land, they caught him and brought him to earth. Forthwith came there hunters and found the hart thereas he lay, and lift him on his feet and would have hewn the head from him. Then said Tristram:

"What will ye do? Never erst saw I hart so quartered, as now ye are about to do. Tell me your craft and your custom wherewith ye are wont to dress your quarry."

Now the master of the hunters was courteous and demure and well nurtured in all manner of gentle deeds. He saw Tristram a right fair man and of noble conditions and by all seeming valiant, and he said unto him thus:

"Friend, gladly will I tell thee our custom. When we have flayed our quarry, we cleave it in sunder from the back, and cut all the limbs in quarters. Other usage have we not learned nor seen nor heard nor received from others. Now if thou understandest somewhat that we have not seen, we grant thee to teach us thereof."

Tristram saith: "God thee thank. This is not the usage in the land whereas I was nourished and born. Now because that I find you kindly to me, then will I, if ye are willing that I be master of this hunt, show you the customs that hunters use in our land."

Then he made ready to divide the hart: when they had flain the beast he cleft it and cut the genitors and the hams from the back: then took he the guts thereout and then the part of the back that was fattest betwixt the shoulders and the part that was fattest behind betwixt the loins. Then he turned the hart over, and took both flanks from him and all the fat parts that were on him, and so severed the limbs from the back. Then he carf the neck asunder, and the head from the neck, and then all the tail, together with the fat of the loins. Then dressed he a long branch, and fixed thereon the heart and the kidneys, liver and lights, and the flesh within the back. Therewith he said to the hunters:

"Now is the hart carved after the usage of our hunters. Dress now the quarry for the hounds."

But they wist not what was the thing whereof he spake. Then took he all the entrails that he had drawn from the hart, and laid them in the hide and led the hounds thither for to devour them. Then said he to the hunters:

"Now take and dress your present, and fix the head of the hart thereon, and bear it afore the king courteously."

Then said the hunters: "By my head, never was it heard in this land of 'quarry' or 'present.' Now sith ye are the first hunter that brought this custom hither, now perform all the craft of a master of the chase and show us these courteous customs, for we know not to do after this usage."

Then Tristram took somewhat from the flesh of all the limbs and thereto the goodliest of the entrails, and cast them again in the hide, and the hounds ate them utterly: and that is the quarry. This the hounds devoured in the hide, and thereof the hunters had marvel. Anon Tristram went into the wood, and cut a stake there as long as might be but such that one might bear it in hand, and he bound to the stake the branch thereas were set the goodliest bits that he had taken from the hart, and fixed the head above on the end, and said to the hunters:

"Sirs, take this now with you, that is called the

present, and bear the head in solemn wise before the King, and let your varlets go before and blow their horns. This hight the 'present.' "

They said: "We wot not how to proceed therewith; natheless we hold better your custom in this than ours. Ye shall follow us before the King, and accomplish before him the 'present,' and we will do all that ye ordain."

Then set they Tristram upon an horse, and his pilgrims followed after him; and he bare on a stake the head of the hart. Anon they came to the court of the King.

Chapter xxii

THEREWITH Tristram took an horn and blew thereon a long, fair note, and all the varlets blew their horns as he bade afore, and there was of them a great company and many horns thereto, and great was the sound of the horns. Then ran out from the hall a great company of the King's servants, wondering and asking what the great blast might betoken. But Tristram and the meynie of hunters stinted not of their blowing ere they were come before the King. And the hunters rehearsed how Tristram had cut in pieces the hart, and how he gave unto the hounds, and concerning the "present," and how they should go to their lord and King blowing notes, for that never tofore in that land were harts so broken in sunder nor the quarry brought home in such solemn wise, nor the King so

TRISTRAM IS BROUGHT UNTO MARK

honored of no man. So it fell thereafter so long as Tristram abode in the King's court, he went often unto the chase and always in the same manner carf he the harts and other beasts that he chased, and brought them to the King after his usage, sith better nor more seemlier was there no usage than Tristram had learned in his land, and even the King's hunters called his usage better.

Now when that night the King had repasted him well, the court sat in the hall for to disport them, some with chess and some with tables, some hearkened songs, other hearkened tales, but the King listed unto harping. Straightway Tristram knew the melody and said unto the harper:

"Harper, play thou well this song. For this made the Bretons in Brittany concerning the love of the good Gurun."

Then said the harper: "What know ye thereof? have ye had perchance a harp-master? In what land have ye learned to pluck the strings, for meseemeth ye know this song?"

"Good master," said Tristram, "in the place thereas erst I dwelt, I learned somewhat of harping for to have solace."

"Take ye the harp," said the minstrel, "and let us hear how thou hast learnt."

Then Tristram took the harp and sounded all the strings and gave the King and all his men so fair harping that full well it pleased him and all that heard, and all praised him for that he had well learned and was nourished in courtesy and was adorned of much meekness and cunning in divers games. He shone with seemly knowledge: never tofore heard they harp struck so fairly in their life-days. When he ceased from his fair playing, the King and many others besought him that he might grant them another melody. Again he soundeth the strings and maketh them another lay, singing and according the harp unto his voice: and in short space he made them a third harping that was so pleasant that all had wondrous liking thereto. Then said the King unto him:

"Worthy friend, may good befall them that bare thee and so nobly nurtured thee. Thou shalt be in my chamber by night and solace me with thy skill and harping when I lie waking."

Thereafter was Tristram welcome of all, beloved and mirthful, debonair and meek: to all was he dear, but to the King dearest, and he had the keeping of his sparhawks, bows and quivers, and the King gave him an horse. All day he was with the King for to delight him, and by night he attended him with harping, and in this wise he used well what he had learned whenas he was young. Now appeareth it that if Tristram had not been ravished away, he had not been known unto the King nor in such good case nor so friended in the land, for now is he dear unto all men, and renowned in that castle and over all that realm.

TRISTRAM HARPETH BEFORE MARK

Chapter xxiii

NOW will we be still as touching Tristram, and say somewhat of his fosterfather, the noble Seneschal, the which wandered widewhere seeking his fosterson, and searched many a land, and was now in toil and labor, in currents and storms of the sea, and in woe of his hard exile, yet gat he no tidings of Tristram. Whenas he came to Denmark, after that three winter were passed sith he departed from home, he heard from a wanderer that Tristram was at the court of King Mark, a mighty and famous prince, and there was he in good case and high esteem, and all loved him and friended him, and he should there still abide for that the King had good liking unto him. When this man told him such tidings, the Seneschal believed him forthwith, for by token that he knew Tristram's apparel he understood the man spake sooth. For this was one of those pilgrims followed Tristram and yode with the hunters unto the King's court, and right truly did he know all Tristram's demeanor and how he stablished him in the King's love and favor.

Now might Roald, the Seneschal, stint of his wandering, and he went unto his vessel and abode a fair wind. When the wind came, he made him ready unto the voyage, and took the sea, and arrived up in England, and so fared on to Cornwall, that marcheth upon England to the west. There dwelt the King and his court, and Roald asked secretly if any might tell him sooth of the matter. They gave him knowledge, whereof he was glad, that it fell unto Tristram that day to serve the King and to stand before his table. Now Roald desired eagerly to find him alone in privity, but whereas a little afore he was richly beseen, now standeth he in ragged weeds: and this poor seeming is all by reason of the hardships and the long journey. He knoweth not how he may cause Tristram to find him, for that he is poorly clad and hath little gold wherewith to clothe him in courtly fashion so that he might enter the court in all honor. Therefore is he dismayed that no poor man is welcome in king's court, and they are welcome only that have enough of richesse. And albeit a man be well born and well nurtured of his conditions, yet if he come to the court poor, there shall he find few will succor him. Now also is Roald come unto the court, yet is he welcome to none, for that none wot who he is nor whence he cometh. At the last it entered his mind that it would scarce avail him if abiding nigh the King he kept himself longer unknown, and he went then unto the gate and called the porter unto him and gave him a gift that he might go in freely. Whenas the porter saw the gift, he opened the door and took him by the hand and led him unto the hall and himself entered, but Roald tarried without. Then when the porter called him, Tristram came out. When Roald beheld Tristram and knew him in certain, he fell forthwith swooning, so rejoiced

THE PORTER OPENETH TO ROALD

him that meeting. Then all they that followed Tristram had marvel wherefore this man that for very happiness swooned away made such lamentation of his joy, and they caught him and lift him up. But weeping and joy both tormented and gladded Roald and made him such happiness that never tofore had he such delight as now he endureth, seeing Tristram there. And straightway when Tristram knoweth him, he so rejoiceth of him and so halseth him with kisses that to none may it be told how either of them loved other. Then Tristram took him by the hand and led him unto the King and said openly in the hearing of all the court:

"My lord the King, this is my kinsman, my father and fosterer, that in many lands hath sought me and now is he rejoiced of finding me. But he hath had sore travail abroad and now seemeth but a poor man. If it please you well to receive him, great joy shall I have of his coming."

The King was gentle and courteous, and called him privily a page and said: "Bring this man unto a chamber and serve him well and give him a rich robe that to thy seeing fitteth him, for he hath been ever a noble man, wise and courteous and well nurtured: therefore shall he be honored of us, for that he was a great helper and joy unto Tristram."

When Roald was clad in seemly wise in rich apparel, then seemed he man of worship and in every limb well-shapen, and whereas he seemed tofore but a churl, now seemed he a lord or an earl. Now is he set at the King's table and sitteth a noble as among nobles: and they eat with pleasaunce, and Tristram serving him courteously.

Chapter xxiv

WHEN they had eaten of the goodly meat and costly drink, they tell tidings of other lands after the custom of courts, what hath happened among princes that dwell in lands nighest thereto, and what hath befallen in the years just past that it behoveth them to know and him to tell. Forthwith Roald recounteth with swift language and ordered words and clear remembrance, before the King and in the hearing of all, what way Rivalon, his lord and prince, had brought away thence Blanchefleur, the King's sister, that he loved, and how he espoused her, and of his death, and how she bare a son and died, and wherefore he let call him Tristram. Then he showeth the King a ring, set with stones of virtue: this had King Mark's father possessed, and the King betaught it unto his sister of his love. And Roald telleth how that Blanchefleur afore her death bade him give this ring unto the King, her brother, for a sure token of her death. Whenas Roald had proffered and the King taken the ring, then the King wist thereby who the young man was. Forthwith of all that company, earls and lords and knights, squires and pages, ladies and gentlewomen, was none that let not fall a tear by reason of that sorrowful adventure, when he rehearsed how sorrowfully was Tristram stolen from him, and how he sought him in many lands with travail and torments. When the King had heard the sooth of these things, he called Tristram unto him with loving words and halsed him and kissed him as his kinsman by adoption and his rightful sister's son. Then went Tristram to his kinsman, the King, and fell on his knees before him, and said:

"Lord, I will that ye grant me arms, and I will go visit my fatherland and heritage, and avenge my father's death, for that I am now of age sufficient to win me my right."

Then said all the lords that sat on either side of the King that well it behoved him so to do, and the King assented unto him and said that he would purvey arms: these arms were right good that the King gave him, wrought of pure silver and gold and set with precious stones. Tristram was purveyed thereto of knights, valiant, goodly, courteous, stout and noble. And two vassals set upon his feet spurs wrought of pure gold. King Mark's self girt on him a sword, and smote him on the neck a great stroke, and thus said:

"Dear nephew, take never stroke from none other man but if ye avenge it forthwith, nor accept none amends nor atonement save stroke for stroke, so long as ye have power to avenge it. So shall ye have renown of your knighthood."

The King then made him a mighty knight, and they led forth for him a goodly destrier and a strong, clad with red trappours, embroidered in gold with

images of lions. And on that day the King gave
him eke horses and arms for a score other young men
for his sake, and a hundred other proved knights,
the which all should follow Tristram to South Brittany to win and defend his right. On the morn
Tristram took leave at the King against his voyage
home with his fosterfather and fellows, and they
came to their ship and went to the board with their
horses and harness. They drew up anchor, and unfurled the sail that was of divers colors, yellow and
blue, red and green, and took the sea, and landed
thereas it best liked them in South Brittany. When
they came unto haven, they landed before the town
cleped Kanoel and they saw there a passing strong
castle, great and fair, that might nowise be taken:
this castle longed unto Tristram's father and still
his men held therein, his lieutenants and vassals.
Then Roald the Seneschal went first from the ship,
and rode unto the castle and let undo all the gates
and entrances. Thereafter came Tristram with his
fellowship, and the Seneschal betaught him all the
keys of the castle, and wrote unto all the barons of
the realm for to come thither and appear before
their lord, the which he had long journeyed and
sought and now by God's help and foreknowing
found. When the dukes and princes, barons and
rich knights were come, Tristram received their
homage and fealty and oaths. And now are all the
folk of his realm in new joy of his return; now are
all the folk that tofore were wroth and troubled
that he was stolen away, free and fain. On the

TRISTRAM APPROACHETH

DUKE MORGAN

morn he made him ready with twenty knights for
to go toward Duke Morgan, and require of him
his rights and lands that he seized from his father.
When he came to the hall of the duke, all the court
arose and hearkened, and Tristram said to the
Duke in this manner:

"My lord Duke, so God you bless as ye have
wrought unto us, for ye hold my realm with wrong
and slewest my father in battle. Rivalon's son am
I, come hither to require my heritage that ye now
hold, howbeit my father owned it aforetime, that
ye yield it unto me with honor and freedom. I am
ready to do you service in so far as a free man
with honor may."

Then answered the Duke: "I have true knowledge
that thou servest King Mark, and he granted thee
good horses and arms and furs and silks, and I perceive thou art a goodly knight. But thou sayest
thou wilt hold realms of me and sayest that I hold
thy possessions with wrong and that thy father I
slew. Now certes I know not wherefore thy prayer
is brought unto me but, as meseemeth, thou seekest
to have ado with me and wouldst make complaints
that thou wilt never bring to deeds. An thou
wouldst win thy realms, wit thou well thou must
win them through force, because the realms thou
callest thine I hold indeed, whether it be with right
or with wrong. As touching that thou layest charges
against me concerning thy father's death, for that
wilt thou need all thy power to maintain it, for never
may I deny nor conceal his death for thee."

Then said Tristram: "Whoso slayeth man and confesseth his death, it behoveth him pay amends unto his friend. Ye avow these things both, that ye had my realms with wrong and ye slew my father. Now here I require you that for both ye make redress, sith neither ye may not deny."

Then said the Duke: "Be silent, thou churl. Thou art full of bobaunce. Thou art a whore's son, and thou knowest not who begat thee, and thou feignest, saying that Rivalon was thy father."

Then waxed Tristram wood for wrath and cried: "My lord Duke, thou liest. For in righteous wedlock was I gotten: that will I make good against thee if thou durst thyself undertake this matter."

When the Duke heard Tristram's word, to wit, that he said he lied, then he sprang up full of wrath and hate, and yode unto Tristram, and smote him in the teeth with all his might with his fist. Then Tristram brayed forth his sword and struck downward upon his head, and clave it down unto the eyes and laid him dead on the floor in the sight of all his court. The fellows and companions of Tristram were full hardy, and drew their swords at once, and drave aback the press that stood on the floor, hewed on both sides and slew whomsoever they might approach. Then Tristram right so soon as he left the hall, leapt upon his horse, and all his fellows on their horses, and took their shields and rode so in an ordered company out of the castle, and he were a fool that then would do them annoy. And then they made of that play a battle, wherein fell more

DUKE MORGAN SMITETH TRISTRAM

TRISTRAM SLAYETH DUKE MORGAN

than an hundred men ere they parted: for now were all the Duke's people harnessed to avenge their lord's death, and there came five hundred men armed at all points and dashed with all the speed they might after Tristram so that those that had swiftest horses drew nigh unto his company.

Chapter xxv

NOW hath Tristram stricken many knights besides Duke Morgan, and he turneth him swiftly to homeward, but the Bretons rode after him a great company and swore that they would avenge their lord upon him. When they that were foremost drew nigh him, Tristram and his men turned them about against them, and withstood them so stoutly that they overcame them all and took their horses, and so widely thereafter they rehearsed their discomfiture that never might the Bretons win renown again. But on that same day Reald the Seneschal let harness a three-score knights with trusty arms and good horses and let send them the same way that Tristram had ridden forth that they should bear succor unto him an he were jeopardied or wished to visit his other castles, so that he might escape his enemies without fear or danger. When now the Bretons overtook Tristram and his men, they wist not whither he should betake him for refuge, and he turned upon them as swiftly and eagerly as he might and smote them were nighest him: but so long they pursued him till at the last came these three-score knights flinging against them, and they set their spears in the rests, and then hewed with their swords. So mightily and eagerly they met the first rank that they slew all that abode them, and those that were behind fled. But Tristram and his fellows followed after and slew them, fleeing like as a flock of sheep runneth, and they won there many horses and all manner arms, and turned them unto their castle with great victory and pris. Of all was Tristram most hardiest and bare the renown, for in all things was he ready and friendly, worthy and worshipful, noble and fortunate. Then he let summon all his liegemen, and when they came he said unto them:

"Friends, I, your righteous lord, am sister's son unto King Mark, and he hath now neither son nor daughter nor lawful heir, wherefore am I his lawful heir. And now I am about to go to him and serve him with all the honor I may. Now grant I to Roald, my fosterfather, this town with all its fees. Then let his son after him take it for the sake of the great toil and hardship that he endured for my sake, and likewise for the loyal care and honorable service that he did unto me in my young days. Be ye now all heedful and obedient unto him. Here give I him my rights and honors. Now will I depart and leave you in friendship."

And he kissed them all and the tears fell from his eyes. Then he mounted upon his horse and his men also, and rode thence to ship, drew up anchor

and unfurled the sail and sailed forth on the sea.
But his barons abode after full of woe, lamenting
his departure, and they were ill pleased that he
would not dwell with them longer but desired so
sore to fare to homeward. And now was their woe
increased of his parting from them.

Chapter xxvi

NOW telleth us the history of Tristram that the
men of Ireland took that time truage of England and many years wrought they so, for the men
of Ireland took much concern for England, for the
King of England that then was knew not to defend
him, though he essayed thereto, and for that cause
was England long time tributary to Ireland. Now
was there also another truage which was made to the
King of Rome of three hundred pounds of pennies.
The men of Ireland took the first year brass and cop-
per, the next winter fine silver, the third winter fine
gold, that should serve unto the needs of all men. In
the fourth year should the King of England and his
men assemble in Ireland to hear law and yield service and fulfill the punishments of all. But in the
fifth year the truage should be three score boys, the
noblest that might be found, and of them were
those to be purveyed that the King of Ireland desired unto himself for squires. And lots were to be
cast among the vassals and other liegemen which
should yield up his boy; but on whom the lot fell

he must send away even were it his only son when the tribute was sent. Now it befell that Tristram landed in England in the haven that he chose, in the same year that the King of Ireland should receive the tribute of boys, and he that was to fetch them was arriven in a rich dromond. For in Ireland was a mighty champion, big and of evil will, a strong man and a fierce, the which was wont every summer to come there to fetch the tribute. And if the tribute be denied him, then will he win it, himself alone, from the defender thereof with strength, for either must one pay the truage or have ado with him.

Now hath Tristram gone from his ship and mounted his horse and ridden up to the castle, whereas the King abode with his dukes and earls, barons and knights, a great company, for they were all summoned thither. There also were comen the noblest ladies with their sons, and they were about to be chosen that should go as tribute to Ireland. All made great lamentation of their sorrow and misery; each feareth for her son lest his lot should come up, for never would it avail to withold or to miss, and rightly was it a peril that they mourned, for by reason of such bondage they must give their sons into exile and peril and woe. Much dole and dolorous shame was it that boys of such worship born were given into such thraldom and servage. Lord God, long-suffering art Thou that endurest such deeds! have pity on their grievous distresses! Noble men wept, women wailed and shrieked, chil-

THE BARONS LAMENT FOR THEIR SONS

THE BARONS IMPLORE GOD'S PITY

dren cried. Mothers cursed the fathers of sons that durst not defend them from bondage against those that would take them, called the fathers coward and recreant, discomfit and shamed for that they durst not fight with Morhaut, that made demand of the truage. The men wist that he was right hardy and grim, mighty in strength and in play of arms, bold in combat and big of his body, and therefore was none found that had not chosen liefer for to yield his son into thraldom and bondage than himself to go unto his death. Therefore, durst no man have ado with Morhaut because that no man weened that he might have the victory. Then when Tristram came into the hall, he beheld there all assembled the mightiest men of all that realm, and they made dole of their woes that they should yield such truage. And Tristram, whenas he saw their grief and heaviness and much weeping, speered what was the cause that they were so dismayed.

"It is," said they, "by reason of the payment of that truage the which Morhaut, ambassador of the King of Ireland, is wont to take. Lo, now is he come to fetch and require it of the nobles of this realm that are now met here together for to cast lots whose son should go."

Then he yode into the hall and into the castle, and if he was tofore unglad now was he grieved the more, for he found the highest barons that were in the realm, and they sat all kneeling before them that should draw the lots, and each besought God to pity him and save him from the evil lot. There beside were the mothers of the children weeping, and the children sobbed and shrieked. Then Tristram waxed hot of heart and said on high:

"Noble lords, God you bless and free you from bondage and thraldom, your shame and disgrace. But marvel me seemeth that in so great company of knights as I now here behold should be found none that durst defend your freedom, and deliver you of thraldom and bondage, nor none that would fight, body for body, to save you on this day from this sorrow that oppresseth you, to the end that never more may these lots be cast nor your children given into thraldom. For certes is this land the dwelling of thralls unless ye will deliver yourselves of this thraldom. Thralls are ye all and no knights if the truage be suffered so to flit away, and all the land to be robbed and pillaged. Great seemeth me your cowardice in so much that ye reck not whither your children go down into bondage and dishonor sith ye deliver them out of your power. Now if ye will have my counsel, then shall ye neither send your children away nor yield truage to this ambassador. Choose ye now among you all one that is most bravest and hardiest in deeds of arms and approved in all knighthood, strong and valiant. He shall stand in single combat against him that now demandeth the truage, and not till he be vanquished and overcomen in the combat let him give you up. But if no man be found nobler than I, then I will well for the sake of the King, mine eme, to fight body for body with such strength as God hath granted me. An Morhaut be mighty, so is God also strong to help me and to deliver your sons and to win your freedom, rather than Morhaut should go forth in such wise with your sons and the portion of gold, unproved and untried, and take with him your wealth and the heirs of your body. Now stand ye up forthwith and let cease of this lot-drawing. Never shall Morhaut boast him that he found us all faint of heart."

Chapter xxvii

THEN spake the King: "Gramercy, fair nephew. Come hither and embrace me. An thou winnest again our freedom, thou shalt be heir of all my realm: no man is worthier to possess it for thou art my sister's son."

Then came Tristram and kissed the King, his eme, and all the vassals and knights that were there, and Tristram gave the King his glove for to make fast the combat with Morhaut. And they all gave him thankings, young men and old, and said that an he might have the better of their enemy and win again their freedom, then would they all love and honor him as their lord, and serve him because he would be their defender. And now they sent after Morhaut, and he weened that they had cast the lots and that he should forthwith take away the boys. Whenas Tristram was ware how Morhaut came in and sat down, he said on loud:

"Hear ye, lords and barons, vassals and knights, young men and old, that Morhaut is now comen hither and saith that ye ought to yield him truage sith each year is he wont to take it. But wit ye well with violence, force, and tyranny is it seized, and with wrong went ye into bondage. For when the men of Ireland made war on you and held strife in England, the men of this land gat neither safety nor peace unto them on none other condition but to pay truage against this tyranny, and sithence ever have given it. But tyranny is not right; rather is it manifest shame: and therefore no truage ought of right to be paid. Ever it is taken with wrong: for whatsomever is taken with force is not rightwise taken, and whatsomever is yielded unto force is ill done according to right judgment. All goods that be seized with robbery be alway ill-gotten, and sith robbery is wrong, then shall Morhaut have naught of us with wrong. If he desireth to take away the boys, yet shall that never be with our goodwill. But forsooth Morhaut saith that he hath right to take them: from his own words will I show none right hath he to take truage here nor to bear it hence, for we will defend us with force and never malgre his force suffer it to depart: that he with force would seize, that will we with force defend. Sith force must needs strive against force, then let him hold the prize that best can win. Certes, we will show unto Morhaut by his own mean that he judgeth all wrong to be right."

Right so when Tristram had thus spoken, Mor-

MARK KISSETH TRISTRAM

haut started up and stood, and he seemed broad of body, big of stature, stout of limb, and right strong, and he cried in loud words from his great throat: "I have understood right well what ye of foolish counsel have said, that ye will not yield me the truage and betake it with goodwill, but rather defend it against me with all your power. But now am I not furnished unto battle, for I have here but a small retinue: when I landed in Britain, I deemed not I had need of such nor that ye should deny me the truage and break your troth and betray me. Sith I be lightly attended and not purveyed unto war, let one of you alone meet me alone for to prove that ye ought not of right this truage pay: then if I fail in this that I have said, then are ye in rightwise manner free. Now if any of your party durst defend, let him forthwith take up my glove."

Tristram was nigh thereto, that was valiant and worshipful, fierce and debonair, and he stood up straightway and went unto him and said: "I am he that will defend against thee that we no truage owe: and we never brake troth unto thee, that will I also defend and prove upon thy body. Go now at once to thine arms, for now shall I go straightway to make ready mine own."

Chapter xxviii

NOW are their troths plight unto the combat, and Morhaut went down unto the seashore and did on his harness. Then he mounted upon a great horse, clad in trusty mail, and he hung on his shoulder his shield, hard and great and thick, and girt himself with a strong sword and a sharp, and so rode unto the field of combat, and made his horse to spring, all the people perceiving how he could ride. But Tristram armed him in the King's court with good hose of steel, and two vassals bound gold spurs unto his feet. Then he did on a trusty hauberk, thick and great, and the King, his eme, girt him with a good sword that was tried in many stours. This sword the King's father had betaught him, together with the ring whereof ye have heard mention afore in this tale, the two treasures that were best in all his realm. Then they set on Tristram's head a shining helm and a bright, the best they might find, and hung on his shoulder a trusty shield, bound with iron and dight with gold, and led before him a red 'horse, all clad in mail. Then Tristram, the good knight, mounted upon his back, and took leave at the King and all his friends. All made great dole for Tristram and all prayed God of grace upon him and Almighty God to bless him and deliver him from the peril, and to grant them the freedom whereof the land was in need: all prayed for him. Then Tristram mounted his horse and hastened to seek combat of his foe and to win the freedom of all England against the ambassador of the King of Ireland. Morhaut is wight and big and orgulous and of great stature: he feareth no knight is in the world. He is the Queen's brother of Ireland, and for her sake he would win the truage: and for this cause the King sent him to England for he knew no man's strength might withstand his strength. But now is one come that will prove his worth.

Then Morhaut held his shield afore him to keep him, and let drop his spear in the rest, and smote his horse with the spurs, and dashed against Tristram. Straightway Tristram put his shield afore him to keep him and set his spear in the rest. When they were met, each smote other in the shield with great might and hard encounter so that the shafts of them both to-shivered, but their shields were so hard that they failed not. Thereupon they lashed out their swords and smote sad buffets that sparks flew from their helms, swords and hauberks. Tristram was fierce in combat, but Morhaut was heavy and tall and proved in many stiff stours. When their defenses failed, each set upon other to work him damage: the helms were dinted with the swords, the hauberks brake, the shields were cloven, the field was covered with iron and steel and golden ornaments from their shields and helms. Neither the men of Ireland nor the citizens might discern who bare him the better nor who had the victory. Then was Tristram right wroth and brandished his sword and smote down on Morhaut's head betwixt shield and helm, and carf in sunder the strap and the helm's brim and a quarter of the shield with its glittering gold and gems, and shore the hauberk from his arm and so much of the flesh as the sword took, and clave in sunder the saddle-bow, and pierced more than a span deep into his horse croup: and this stroke had gained more, had his shield been longer. But when Morhaut saw him do so, he lashed at him, for Tristram held the shield far from him, and the sword struck his left breast, and the hauberk proved false under that stroke, and there was a great wound thereas the sword bit, and well-nigh he must have slain him. Then Morhaut said to him:

"Now it appeareth that thou followest wrong. Better were it that thou yield the truage than thou wert so shent and shamed. For all are wounds mortal that my sword maketh, for it is empoisoned of both edges. Never may no leech come that can heal this wound but only my sister. She only knoweth the nature of all herbs and their virtue and all manner of salves that may heal wounds. Yield thee as wounded and discomfit and vanquished, and I will well for love of thee bring thee unto the Queen, and make her heal thy wound. Then will we be always fellows together, and all my wealth shall be in thy power, for never found I no knight that I might so praise as thee."

Then answered Tristram: "For none of these services thou offerest me will I leave my valor and

MORHAUT WOUNDETH TRISTRAM

TRISTRAM SLAYETH MORHAUT

prowess. Much liefer will I die in battle, than with cowardice fordo mine honor. Never will I do so ill for any wound that I have yet felt. God is almighty to help me, and of his mercy to defend our freedom against thee. I avaunt me that I will yet be mine own avenger: stroke for stroke will I quit thee, so that England will be in peace for thee evermore. Now art thou full of joyance, but this night thou shalt no more be on live."

All were dolorous and of heavy heart, men and women, when they espied Tristram's horse bebled, and prayed God He should deliver him of torment and danger. Tristram heard their words, and he saw how that Morhaut set upon him, and he brandished his sword with great might and smote upon his helm. The iron failed, the steel sundered, the war-coif availed not, and he shore away the hair and beard, and the sword stack in the brainpan and brains. But Tristram pulled at his sword, for he would have it ready an there were need, and he pulled his sword to him with all his strength: and there was left in the brainpan so much of the sword as had stuck therein. But Morhaut fell from his horse dead, and then said Tristram:

"If forsooth Ysolt, the Queen, alone hath knowledge of poisons and none other may me help, yet will she never have cunning enough to help nor heal thee, howsoever my wound fareth, for that thy wound is the deadlier and more loathly."

Then bade he the ambassadors to bear away Morhaut's body to Ireland and say that never shall they get truage of England, neither gold nor silver, but only this gift. Then the men of Ireland took up his body and with great sorrow bare it to the strand to his tent, and did off his harness, and bare him to the ship, and drew up cable and anchor, and sailed forth to sea home to Ireland, and told their tidings, the which made all the people of Ireland to mourn.

Chapter xxix

NOW rode Tristram home to the King's court, and they took from him all his harness, and sent for all the leeches that in the realm were best for a wound that was poisoned. And he drank then a drink of treacle and divers herbs and let put a plaster upon him to draw out the venom. But he was in sharp torments, and the King and the court and the people in great sorrow, for all doubted that he must die. His wound grew black and took no allegiance, neither for herb nor for drink. Then they arrayed for him a fair closet and let hang it with costly stuffs that he might lie there quietly.

Now have the men of Ireland arrived up in the full fair haven of Dublin, and they took the body of Morhaut and laid it on his shield and carried it up the street, and there was much lamentation of all the people at the fall of Morhaut, brother unto the noble Queen Ysolt, and all the citizens said: "Unhappily was that truage claimed." Then the

MORHAUT IS CARRIED TO THE STRAND

amabassadors took the body and bare it up to the castle, and the barons ran thither to behold the dead knight. Then said the ambassadors unto the King with loud and bold speech:

"Mark, King over all England, sendeth you these words, to wit, that him behoveth to pay you none other truage than this dead knight. But if ye will again require it and send an ambassador thither, him also will he send you back dead. A young man in that country, the King's sister's son, bold and puissant, surmounted the might of Morhaut and delivered him to us dead, unto our woe. He is new comen to the King's court, and there is no man found mightier than he."

Whenas the King saw Morhaut dead, he sighed from his heart, and felt great sorrow, and lamentation arose through all the court. And anon the noble Ysolt heard these tidings, and she went from her chamber unto the hall, and when she beheld her brother dead, she fell on the body in a swoon, and much she wept his death. And she cursed England and England's truage and the malfortune of Morhaut: and she cursed him that slew him and the land that owed the truage. Therewithal espied they the piece of the sword that was broken and stack in his brainpan. Then they took a tongs and drew it out and gave it unto Ysolt: she let wash it forthwith of the brains and blood, and put it in her coffer for to keep in remembrance of the wrong, for therewith was he slain. Then they let inter Morhaut's body with all the honor they might.

Chapter xxx

NOW speak we of Tristram, that now let bind and salve his wound, but found no leech in that land might heal it. Then had he much travail of the wound in such sort that he were liefer dead than living in so great pain. Never might he win rest nor sleep because the venom was fast in his bones and flesh, and full loth were all his kin and friends to sit beside him by reason of the stench that issued from him. Then said Tristram unto the King:

"Lord, I require thee for thy love's sake recomfort me somewhat of this grievous life, and offer me counsel in my misery. None of my kin and friends will come unto me nor visit nor solace me. Therefore will I depart hence, wheresoever God may suffer me to go according to His mercy and my need."

When Tristram had ended his speech and made complaint of his woe unto the King, then said the King:

"That were great folly, dear nephew, that thou wouldst fain slay thyself. Surely such a chance may befall in a day as may not be wrought in a twelvemonth, and in like wise may succor come to thee in short space. But sithen thou art minded to depart, I will purvey thee a boat with all thing that thou needest to have with thee."

Tristram gave thank to the King, but the King

MARK VISITETH TRISTRAM

TRISTRAM HARPETH IN THE RUDDERLESS BOAT

and all other grieved of his departure. Therewith
was a vessel garnished with victual enough and
whatso him needed: and all followed him unto the
boat and mourned his departure, and he took the
sea, and all they that abode after prayed that God
would guard him and pity him. And he was driven
on the sea, what by wind and what by flood, so long
that he wist not whither he went, but at the last he
touched Ireland, and it was told unto him forthwith
whereunto he was arrived. And Tristram was now
adoubted of his landing that the King and his other
enemies should learn who he was, and he let call
him therefore by the name Trantris. Now hath he
shown his harping and his gentle arts that he knew,
and incontinent there went forth tidings concerning him and his manifold cunning. When Ysolt,
the King's daughter, the noble and debonair, gat
these tidings of him, much she desired to see him
and somewhat of his manifold cunning, and she
asked of her father and mother that she might go
thither. Now hath the Princess Ysolt caught great
desire to require her father and Queen Ysolt, her
mother, to put her under his teaching, for she would
fain learn in the beginning to harp and to write letters and to make verses. And so he came unto the
Queen's chamber, but men might not endure him
within for the stench that rose from his wound, and
piteous seemed it unto the Queen, and she said unto
him:

"Gladly will I help thee for the sake of Ysolt,
my daughter, to the intent that thou mayest teach

her unto thy power, with kindness and goodwill, whatsomever thou knowest and she desireth to learn, if by fortune I may heal thee."

Then spake she unto a maid: "Make ready anon my remedies of poisons."

And all that day she laid on him a plaster, and anon the stench came out of the wound, and the night next after the Queen took the wound with her own hand and washed it out with healing balms and bound it with marvelous plasters so that within short space she did away the swelling and the venom. In all the world leech was there none so knowing of all manner arts of healing, for she could how to help all manner diseases and wounds wherewith men may be visited. She was cunning in the virtues of all herbs that may be used unto any good, and wist all devices and means that pertain unto leechcraft. She knew thereto how to give succor against poisonous drink, and to heal poisonous wounds and perilous pains and all manner swellings, and to draw the smart out of all limbs, so that nowhere was to be found one more skilled nor of leechdoms a better master. When she had opened the wound and drawn forth all the stinking flesh and withdrawn the poison every dele, then all the living flesh seemed the better. Thereafter she bound on with her finger a plaster and healing ointment thereon so oft and skilfully that within a XL days he was as well healed as he had never caught wound: and hath become so strong and all perfect as he was erst. Then strove Trantris with all

TRISTRAM TEACHETH YSOLT TO HARP

diligence to learn Ysolt both night and day to strike
the harp and all manner of stringed instruments, to
write and make letters, and knowledge of all crafts.
And now hath Ysolt learnt much of him, and over
all that realm waxed her fame for all manner of
learning that she had learned of him through study;
and her mother rejoiced that she had learned of
Trantris goodly graces and wide fame of wisdom,
and thereto was her father right glad that she had
learned so much in so short space, and he sent for
her to play the harp for disport before him and
before his court. Moreover, she showed her wisdom in divers questions and answers that she made
before the wisest men. Right great joy had the
King of her night and day, for he had no child but
her only, and she was his most solace.

Chapter xxxi

WHEN Tristram knew himself healed and fully
restored of his body and to have recovered
flesh and strength and comeliness, then he studied
many ways how he might escape out of Ireland, for
he durst no longer there abide: he doubted him he
might become known and whence he was, and therefore he went ever adread lest any man met him
that might perchance know him. And he took this
counsel and device, and came another day unto the
Queen, and kneeled before her and bespake her with
fair and loving words:

[87]

"I give you thankings, worshipful lady, of God and all saints for your gracious labor and kind attendance and worshipful dealing in so much as ye have healed my wound and solaced my woe and worthily restored me. Faithful and subject shall I be in your service, and in all ways it behoveth me show you worship and entire loyalty and changeless love. And now would I of your leave repair me to my home and visit my friends and kin, but so long as I be on live, am I your servant. My kin and friends know not whither I am become nor if I be quick or dead, for when I departed I purposed to fare unto Spain, for I was fain to learn the lore of the stars and hidden matters. But now would I fain visit my friends and solace their fears. Prepare ye my boat, and I will now with your leave depart. God you thank and reward of all your good works that ye have me graciously and mercifully done in so far as I had need."

Then said the Queen: "My friend, your vessel shall be ready so soon as ye will it. And so ever it endeth to harbor a stranger, for now ye forsake us for the sake of your kin as soon as we be full fain to keep you, and ye esteem little our labor though much have we done for you. But sithen ye will not longer serve us, we will not hold you with force. Ye shall have your boat garnished and forthwith shall ye go, by God's leave and ours, whithersoever it please you. And now I bestow on you for your dispenses a mark of pure gold."

Tristram took the gold and thanked her of her

manifold kindness and mercy and goodly gifts and sufficient bounty. Howbeit, an the Queen might have counseled him, she had liefer that he had not departed so suddenly. And so Tristram took his harp and went unto his boat, solacing him therewith, and his boat was purveyed of all those things that him needed. Then he went to the board, gat a fair wind and sailed forth to sea.

Chapter xxxii

SO happily went Tristram froward Ireland that he landed up where he would in Britain, in the haven under the King's castle: and they that were without the castle straightway knew Tristram's ship, and forthwithal leapt into a boat and asked where Tristram was, and found him whole and merry, and saluted him and had much joy of him, and he departed from the ship. And they led unto him a great horse and a stout, and he mounted and rode so home unto the castle. And there ran unto him the servants of the King and welcomed him, both young and old, and made great joy that he was come back out of death. When the King also heard these tidings, he rose straight and went to meet him and saluted him blithely and kissed him, and when the King was set beside him, Tristram told the King of his voyage, and where he had been, and who had healed him. And Tristram rehearsed how in Ireland had he been succored and how he had used craft and deceit to help him, and how the Queen's self had healed him with goodly usage and mighty medicines.

Great marvel had all the court of these tidings, for they had weened all that he was so feeble and ill bestead when he went away that never might he win back nor visit them again. And some said that he must have witting of magic arts and sleights to have come forth from the midst of such foes, and other said that he knew to turn the tempers of men, and they said that he would avenge him on all that in his malady forsook him. Yeomen and knights, barons and the mightiest men that were in Britain were wroth with Tristram for his knowledge and cunning, and for that he would be king after his uncle, and would then desire vengeance and work damage to them that shamefully shunned him in his misery and sickness. And so they made secretly a plot against Tristram, for they feared him and bore rancor to him by reason of his nobleness and wisdom and good fortune. Then they opened unto the King what they had devised, that it behoved him to wed and get him an heir, male or female, as God willed, to rule his realm and hold it after his days, and they gathered all together before the King, and brought him their counsel and showed and made clear unto him that if he should not wed soon a wife so that he might have an heir to guide the realm after his death, then were it much to fear that strifes should rise and any man might raise himself unto their lord that with wrong should claim the throne; and therefore they said also they would nowise serve the King more but if he approved their counsel. Then said the King:

"I give you thanks for your goodwill in so much that ye desire mine honor and have regard unto my worship, that I should win me a bride and have an heir to hold my realm after my lifedays. I wot well ye be not afeard of war, yet is it good to take thought for peace. Now sith this is for mine honor, I will gladly listen your counsel, and do ye find me a maiden that will be my peer in lineage and wit and nurture, beauty and courtesy, gentleness and seemly conditions, that I may not wed out of my degree. Then will I gladly do that ye bid me. Ye are my liegemen sworn, and it fitteth not that your plan be opposed unto mine."

"Grant us then, my lord," said they, "to consider, and assign us a day for speech, and we will seek for thee a marriage that is full noble so that we will not get shame thereof but rather thy thanks and entire goodwill. So sith thou layest the fulfilling of this counsel upon us and our judgment, we will so accomplish it for thee as thou wilt thyself desire it."

Then spake the King: "I will well that so it be. I set you XL days hence: show me then your devising, and if it like me, I will gladly follow it, if it appeareth good."

Chapter xxxiii

NOW when the summons day came, they came all before the King. For they wished him to wed that they might betray Tristram: seldom do men let him enjoy peace whom they are resolved to hate. They desire now that the King take him a wife that he may get of her an heir. But the King will at no cost take no wife save one that is equal to him in blood, and wise and courteous in all her conditions, renowned and of fair worship; and on this plea, that he will have none other than he hath afore said, he seeketh to escape their wiles.

"My lord, the King," said one of them, "on this day ye summoned us for to name unto you a woman that it may beseem you with reason and honor to take for your royal queen, and that is not of lineage lower than ye be, and that is such as ye have bidden us choose for you. Now have ye ofttimes heard that the King of Ireland hath a fair daughter and so gifted of Nature that for goodness and noblesse she lacketh for naught that a woman's conditions ought to have. She is the most famous and fairest, the wisest and most courteous in all knowledge of all the women that as at this time men know in all Christendom, and her parage is not unknown to you, to wit, that she is daughter unto a king and queen. Now if ye will not take this maiden, it seemeth us indeed as ye would have no wife at all and get you none heir unto your realm.

Tristram, your sister's son, knoweth and is witness thereto that we have chosen for you her that we know for noblest, for even greater to our knowledge is the rehearsal of her goodness."

Then was the King silent a space and pondered an answer and said: "If it were so that I would have her, in what wise might I come unto her where her father and all her people hate me and all my people, so that they would fain slay every living wight that is in this land? And I fear me an I send my men that he would scoff at them and slay them and deny me his daughter: and that would be to me great despite and scorn and a shameful ending, and mine enemies would say that dread of him constrained us to ask his daughter."

"My lord," said one of his vassals, "it oft betideth that in divers countries kings make war together in long hatred and manifold woes and slaughter; then they amend their wrath and hate, and turn malice to peace, and wrath unto love through wedding of their daughters and sisters, and enchieve most excellent friendship through birth of common children. Now an we may compass this alliance and marriage with peace and joy, then may it well come to pass that ye shall rule all Ireland, for the Princess Ysolt is only child unto the King of Ireland."

Then said the King: "If this thing may be advanced and performed with worship, I will indeed have none other but her, for Tristram hath much praised her courtesy and wit and all conditions that may become a woman. Now consider ye how we shall attain unto her, for never will I take other if I may have her not."

Then said the earl: "My lord, no man is there in the world able to win her save only Tristram, your nephew. He knoweth the King and the maiden, and he is nigh friend unto the Queen. He hath knowledge of the Irish tongue, and all Ireland is known to him. If he will heartily endeavor, then will he surely win her, either by cunning, or art or force, or it may be the King will give her in marriage with goodwill."

Chapter xxxiv

NOW hath Tristram listened their speech that they have spoken before the King urging him that he be now surely wedded, and he understood that he will take none other but Ysolt. Moreover he perceived that his uncle had none heir of his body that might rule his realm after his day, and he bethought him that if he refused the journey, he would make men to suspect and deem that he would have none other heir but himself. So discovered he their guile and engine and secret devices, and he answered them wisely and calmly:

"My lord King, be ye rightwise judge touching this journey unto the which ye have appointed me. Ireland, certes, is known to me and the customs of the men thereof: known to me are the King and all his noblest men, the Queen and the Princess Ysolt. But I slew the Queen's brother, and if I go thither and ask the maiden in marriage, and the King wot who I am, be ye siker he will never let me return on live. But that I may not make an enemy of you nor of none other, and because I will that mine uncle have a lawful heir, I will gladly go to further mine uncle's worship, and so will I work, as God may suffer me, unto mine uttermost power and knowledge. I will indeed go into Ireland to perform this errand, and if I may not win Ysolt, will I come again never more."

Then he made ready his going, and chose of the King's people a score which he knew most valiant and fair and strong of all the court, together with the best arms and good horses, and they went so on ship, purveyed of victual sufficient and good drink and much gold, and laden with good wheat and flour and honey, wine and all the goodliest drinks that men may have at need. Now is their ship manned, and they sail forth on their errand unto their enemies. And Tristram knoweth not how he will ask the maiden, nor by what craft he should fetch her unto the ship and sail away with her. And if he ask her of the King, then may it well hap that she be forthwith denied him. Yet to carry her off from so mighty father and kinsmen, he findeth no device how it may be. And he spake of this before his fellows, but none of them might give no answer nor make no conclusion, but rather they bewailed their errand and made dole and cursed the King's councilors that had devised such an errand for them. So sailed Tristram across the Irish Sea, and was right heavy and full of thought, and him seemed it would rather behove them if he might bear Ysolt with him on the ship and haste away with her; for he had now concluded that they would give themselves out as merchants, and would long tarry there to find some fine craft and study how he might best with good cunning come unto her and most privily. Now they sailed so night and day till they cast an anchor before Dublin, and they launched their boat and sent two of their knights to get leave of the King, and peace and freedom to sell their wares. When these knights came unto the King they bespake him with fair words, for they were well used in all courteous customs.

Chapter xxxv

WHEN they had saluted the King they said: "We be merchants and fare from land to land with our goods to win us gold, for we know not how to work in other manner. We loaded our vessel in Brittany and purposed us for Flanders, but when we took the sea, there came a storm against us and drave us long space with much hardship till that we came hither to haven; and we learned that food was hard to buy in Ireland, and therefore came we hither heavy-laden with victual. Now if we may have license of you to sell in peace our wine and provision, then will we bring our vessel into haven and lay out our goods unto cheaping; but an ye will it not, we will sail unto other countries."

Then answered the King: "Leave I give unto you, peace and freedom, to sell here as pleaseth you. No man shall mischief you nor do you no wrong. Ye shall have right fair welcome, and freedom to return whensoever ye will."

When they had gotten leave of the King, they gave him thanks, and went to ship and sailed within the haven, made fast and pitched a pavilion, ate and drank, and played divers games till the day was ended. No chaffer did they make, but they solaced them with great cheer and held speech with courteous knights of gentle customs. But on the morn as soon as they awoke, they heard rise in the streets shouting and woe of men and women, and next were they ware how the folk fled down to the sea for to succor them from the anger and fear of a dreadful dragon that was in the realm and every day wont to come unto the town and work such harm unto the people that he slew all that he might come nigh with the fire, that he blew from him. In all the realm was no man so strong and bold that he durst abide him. All the knights and men of the town that heard his coming fled down to the strand to save them. The King had let cry over all the realm that if any were so trusty knight as to slay the dragon, he should have his daughter and the half of his realm with all honor for him and his

heirs. And that had the King written down and
ensured with his troth in hearing of all the baronage
of his realm: and many had emprised it, the which
the dragon had slain, so that none was so valiant
and trusty he durst abide him or come in his path:
they that were mightiest ran straightway to cover
them. Now whenas Tristram beheld them so running, he asked the men of Ireland what ailed them
and why they ran so: and they told him what was
betid, both touching the dragon and the guerdon that
the King had set for him should kill the dragon.
Then he ascertained fully where the dragon haunted
by night and at what hour he wont assail the citizens,
and he tarried till evening so that he told no man
his intent, and he spake with the captain of his ship,
and he let take his horse and saddle and all his
harness, and when the day dawned, he armed him
at all points.

Chapter xxxvi

THE dragon held his wont to assail the citizens
at dayspringing. When Tristram was least
ready, he heard the noise and leapt forthwith upon
his horse so that none of his fellows was ware save
only his squire. He then drave his steed with the
spurs and hasted the best pace he might up to the
rocks whereas the dragon abode at night. While
he rode in such wise, there met him withal a great
company of knights, the which fled before the

TRISTRAM ENCOUNTERETH

THE DRAGON

dragon on swift horses, and armed at all points, and
they shouted unto him anon and bade him turn
again after them as fast as he might so that the
dragon that was full of venom and flame, should
not slay him. And he would by no mean turn him
again for he was purposed to approve his puissance.
And he looked now tofore him and was ware how
the dragon came crawling, and bare 'his head on
high and shot forth his eyen and tongue, and blew
from him on all sides poison and flame, so that
whatsomever thing that liveth, when it came afore
him, he slew and destroyed the same with fire. As
soon as the dragon espied Tristram, he bellowed
and all swelled up, but Tristram waxed valiant in
mind for to prove his prowess and drave the horse
with the spurs and set his shield afore him. And
he thrust the spear in the mouth of the beast with
such random and wrath that all his teeth that withstood the dint flew wide from his skull, and the iron
pierced forthwith to his heart and out at his belly,
so that Tristram buried a piece of the shaft in his
body and neck, but the fire that the dragon threw
from him slew and destroyed the horse. But Tristram leapt lightly from his back, and drew his sword
and set upon the dragon and hewed him asunder
in the midst. Now whenas the dragon lay dead,
he went to his head and cut the tongue from his
skull and set it within his hose and went away,
for he would not that men saw him. Then he
espied a mere that stood in a dale by a certain
shaw and he went thither forthwith. Whenas he

was nigh comen unto the mere, the tongue grew
hot within his hose, and he was smitten in 'his
breathing by the reek of the tongue, and it poisoned
all his body and bereft him his speech and brought
him anon into unwit and he waxed all dark, black,
and swollen. And he lay in this plight, woeful and
strengthless for the poison, so that he might not
get to his feet nor have help save he received pity
of other men.

Chapter xxxvii

THE King had a seneschal, which was a man
right orgulous, and of his parage Irish, and
he was full of malice, sleights and wiles, and false
and a liar. And he presumed for to love Ysolt,
the King's daughter, and for love of her each day
he armed him against the dragon, but whensoever
he beheld him, he hasted away on his horse with all
the speed he might, so dismayed and fearful that
though at that time were offered unto him all the
gold of Ireland, he durst not look behind him into
the eyen of the dragon. Now whenas Tristram
rode against the dragon, this seneschal was ware
of it, but albeit he was armed at all points, with
drawn sword in hand, he durst not come one whit
nearer, thereas aught might do him damage, ere
he perceived that the dragon must be dead. But
when he saw not Tristram nowhere, but there lay
his sword and shield and the horse dead, then he

supposed the dragon both to have slain the horse and swallowed Tristram. Then took he the bloody sword and smote off the head of the dragon therewith, that it might grow unto his honor that in certain he had slain the dragon. Then went he riding his horse and shouting with a great steven through the town, and said:

"I have slain the dragon! I have slain the dragon! Now, O King, have I freed your realm and avenged your men and your despites. Yield me forthwithal my warison, which is Ysolt your daughter. For that, certes, was your promise, unless your faith fail me."

When the King heard this thing that he had suffered himself aforetime to do and to will, he said: "I will this evening assemble my councilors, and tomorn will I tell thee early and hold all that I have afore promised."

When this matter was spread abroad that the King's daughter was to be given away and men came unto her chamber and she had understood it, then wit ye well she was heavy and dolorous, for no fiend of hell she hated more than this seneschal that had thought for to love her. Never might she love him though she should possess all the world's wealth in bridal-gift, and she said unto her mother:

"Never may I assent thereto that my father purposeth to bestow me upon that evil man: never may God will me such malfortune that I must take him. Sooner will I destroy me with a knife than come in the danger of this treacherous and deedless man.

Whence should come such deeds and prowness, valor and knighthood upon him that among doughty company hath been fearful and a coward ever? How might this dreadful serpent be slain of him that every man of this land knoweth that he is reproached of cowardice and never hath proved him good? Never may I trow he hath slain the serpent, nay, even that he might look back upon him whilst he was on live. But rather is it that he proclaimeth this lie for he would fain attain unto me. Mother," said she, "let us go forth now and see the dragon and espy who hath slain it and when he died, for certes some man of this people must know to tell somewhat thereof."

Then said the Queen: "I will well do as pleaseth you, my daughter."

They prepared them to depart from the castle through a certain privy door that led to the garden. Then they yode by the narrow path that lay from the garden forth into the field, and found there the dragon lying dead, and the horse before him in the sand, but the horse all brent and swollen that it was a passing great marvel.

"Our Lord knoweth," said Ysolt, "that never did the Seneschal own this horse. It is the knight that owned this horse that hath slain the serpent, wheresomever he have now become."

Then they espied the shield, gilt with the brightest gold and on it a fair painture done.

Chapter xxxviii

"BY my faith, mother," said Ysolt, "never the
Seneschal bare this shield, for this is newly
made and gilt within and without, and it is not after
the fashion of this country. He that bare it hath
avenged our wrongs upon this serpent; but our vile
Seneschal boldly demandeth the payment of another's deed. This valiant knight he must have
murthered."

Then they went about a space further till they
saw Tristram whereas he lay, and when they found
him they perceived him blackened and swollen.
Then they wist that he was poisoned, and dolorous
it seemed them, and the Queen mourned his jeopardy. And she put her hands upon him and found
him quick and warm, and she took out from her bag
that which men call poison-herb and put it in
his mouth betwixt his teeth and treacle therewith.
Forthwithal was he purged of the power of the
poison, and the weakness fell from his heart, and
then he opened his eyes and mouth, and said clearly:

"O my Lord God, never tofore knew I my body
so heavy. Who are ye, and where am I become?"

"Fear not," said the Queen, "this malady shall
not harm thee, by God's will. Thou shalt soon be
well of thy sickness."

Then servants of the Queen bare him home thence
so privily that no man had knowledge nor witting
of this save they. When they came with him unto

the Queen's chamber, they took from him his arms and found in his weeds the dragon's tongue. Then the Queen dressed a healing plaster and laid the mighty plaster on his body withoutforth to draw the poison from him, and withinforth she treated his body with powerful healing drafts so that he felt all his body soothed. None other leech had he save the Queen, and none other esquire save the Lady Ysolt, which served him humbly. And ofttimes he thanked them of their manifold toil and goodness that gave him help and life from the poison that was in his body. The morrow early came the Seneschal before the King's court and held in his hand the dragon's head, and went before the King and said on high:

"My lord the King, listen my words. Ye let proclaim and publish that he that slew the serpent should have your daughter. Now require I of you that ye hold your forward with me and royal promise: let your gift be seen and vouchsafe me your daughter in marriage. Here may ye behold the head of the dragon, the which I cut off with my sword."

Then said the King: "Certes shall my word be holden." And he called unto him two knights and said unto them: "Go ye to the Queen's chamber and say that she come unto me, and also my fair daughter, the damozel Ysolt."

When the knights were comen thither they bare the message of the King after the manner that was bidden them. The Princess Ysolt said she might at no cost go there, for so much was she tormented of her head and her limbs that she might take none rest nor sleep, and she asked the King by her honor that she might have quiet that day and rest, for now might she by no mean go unto him. But the Queen arose and went with the knights unto the King, and they all, the King and Queen and their councilors, put the matter in respite, and a day was appointed unto the Seneschal.

Chapter xxxix

WHEN now a day had been set for the Seneschal, the lords repaired unto their homes. And in the mean while the fellows of Tristram sought him widewhere in the fields and woods, roads and forests, and they made great dole of his loss that he had forsaken them. They wist not what emprise to begin nor what rede it most beseemed them to hold, whether to turn again or to abide there, for they wist not what was him betid. Natheless is he well kept in the Queen's court, and the Queen herself hath healed him and he hath won again his health and strength. And the Queen said unto him:

"Friend, what be ye or whence are ye or how slew ye the dragon? Much ye resemble Trantris, the which was afore right famous here. Ye may be peradventure his near kinsman: of what estate be ye?"

[109]

Tristram told the Queen what him list of the lineage of them both. "My lady, I am of Flanders born, and am comen hither for to sell merchandise, and we brought our ship to land with the King's leave and his welcome and assurance of peace. And on a day I armed myself as other knights do, and rode forth to inquire touching this great serpent that to my hearing wrought harm upon all the folk of his land. I would well prove my prowess and knighthood upon that grimly dragon. It happed by God's will I slew him, and I took the tongue from his head and put it within my hose. And so was I burned with the poison and swollen all over that I weened well I might die, and I hied me unto the mere, and then fell I in such a swoon that I wist not who came unto me. God grant I give good thank to those gave me succor, and to them will I do my devoir with whatso services I can."

Then answered the Queen: "Friend, it was I came unto you as at that time, and I let bear you hither secretly, and I drew out the venom from you, and now are ye whole. If ye reward us well of our labor, then ye will do as a wise knight and a courteous and a worshipful bachelor: and now will we tell you, friend, what we would have to our reward, and if ye be a good bachelor as well we deem you to be, then may ye give us aid. Our Seneschal saith unto the King that he hath slain the dragon, and he claimeth to have my daughter, Ysolt, unto his guerdon, and therewith the half of our realm and kingdom, and the King hath will to give

her unto him in marriage, but that will she never.
For he is a fool and puffed up with pride, hard and
malicious, fickle as an harlot that is true to no man,
a treacher and envious, hateful and a coward, and
blemished with many other defaults no noble man
ought to have. For this cause will the Princess
Ysolt consent unto him never, and sooner will she
slay herself, for it accordeth not together, her
noblesse and his manifold vices, though he should
bestow upon her whatsoever is precious in the
world. Now have we assigned him a day to take
her, but if we make it good against him that he
slew not the dragon. Ye know the certainty that he
was not the slayer thereof. If ye will undertake
to defend the damozel and all the realm from him,
then ye show us great honor and service and such
love as we deserve: and ye will win renown over all
our kingdom for your goodness and valor and
thereto will ye win the damozel and a great domain:
for the King must in sooth grant you the damozel
in marriage and the honor withal that was aforetime
promised."

Then spake Tristram: "God wot, for the sake of
your love will I make the Seneschal deny his oath,
for never destroyed he the serpent nor never were
his hands nigh what time I slew him. And if he
will have ado touching this matter, I will defend
the Princess Ysolt from him, and never shall he take
her, for with falsehood, lies, and treachery hath
he sought her. Vainly ye had given unto me my
life again, should I now refuse to serve you and

succor you in such manifest dangers and sure need.
Now if it liketh you and ye be nowise against it,
I would my squire came unto me for I would know
what hath befallen our company of merchants and
my fellows. I wot well they been in doubt that they
wist not what hath of me becomen, nor whether I
be quick or dead. Wit ye well they have sought
me and searched, and know not whether I be on
live or dead."

Then answered the Queen: "Fain will I do that
pleaseth you." And she sent then a lad of hers that
most was of her privity, to bid Tristram's squire
come unto him, for he would speak with him of his
need and of his fellows and how it fared with them.

Chapter xl

NOW speaketh Tristram with his squire and
saith him that he should do his fellows to wit
all that was befallen him sith that he departed from
them, and how he is in great delight and honored
of the Queen and the Princess Ysolt. Then repaired
the squire unto the seashore and told the tidings
first unto their captain, and the captain rehearsed
it before the knights, how Tristram had slain the
dragon, and touching the forward that was made
concerning the damozel and half the domain of the
King of Ireland. Then were they all recomforted
and plucked up their heart and it seemed they caught
new courage by reason they wist him whole and

living, and they sold all their wine and with much friendship they thanked the citizens, so great joy had they of the tidings they had received of Tristram: and they made a full good sale of wines and victuals, honey and flour and wheat, and they won the friendship of every man and good liking of all the people and pleasant cheer. Now Ysolt set her thought for to serve Tristram fairly, how she might best solace him with all manner of food that his body required for strength and puissance, until the King of Ireland proclaimed unto his court, the lords and barons over all his realm, that he would give away his daughter and hold his word with the Seneschal. Tristram sent unto his fellows that they should come unto the court with the barons of the King, and forthwith they arrayed them in fine woven apparel and all of one color, and their nether weeds of divers colors, and underneath with white skins and sable and the best silks wrought with mickle art, so that if each of them had been a full worshipful king of a great realm they might not be better beseen. And they mounted upon their horses with their gear and golden saddles, and rode two by two unto the King's court and alight from their steeds before the steps of the King's hall. And their horses were right big and well proved in hard stours: they stamped their feet and neighed that it might be heard all over the King's court. The fellows of Tristram were men right goodly and right stiff in fight: they went into the hall and ordered themselves courteously next unto the greatest lords and on the highest floor, fairly and with pleasaunce: rich was that company in seeming and noble their array. Then spake the men of Ireland with themselves:

"Fair is the meynie of these Flemings, and much more rich must be a meynie of Flemish kinghts, an such be the merchants of that land, for of our men none are so noble as these."

Chapter xli

WHEN all were set, the Queen was led honorably into the hall, and with such worship as beseemed her, and sat down nigh unto the King, but Tristram, that followed her, sat next unto the Princess Ysolt, a likely man and fair of his eyen and richly robed. All had marvel that saw him what he might be, for well they wist he was not of Ireland, and each asked of other, but none might tell what he was. Now stood up in haste in that great, thick press of nobles and barons that was there the Seneschal, and he ruffled and puffed him up, and said on high:

"My lord the King, hearken ye this my business on this day that ye summoned me hither. It behoveth you to hold your covenant unto me, to wit, that he that slew the dragon should wield your daughter and the half of your realm. Behold, of how great valiance and prowess am I: before a great fellowship of knights I slew the dragon and smote off his head with one stroke of my sword, and ye may now behold how I have brought hither his head. Now because I have slain him I require you, my sovereign lord and king, that ye deliver unto me the maiden. Howbeit, an ye will not your foreward keep, then am I ready for to defend my claim and maintain my right, if any man be that will refuse or defend it against me, to the end that the court may judge and wise men decide betwixt us."

"By my faith," said then the Princess Ysolt, "a churl and a gander is he that demandeth payment and wages for his labor. After another manner must he win his guerdon, else shall he never achieve it. Certes, that knight knoweth not what he doeth the which claimeth for himself another's deed and vaunteth unto him another's prowess. All too little did the dragon withstand thee that thou shouldst for this and naught else win me and a great domain. Methinketh thou must greater things emprise for to win me and so great domain than to show here the dragon's head. Small toil is it to bear it hither to the King's court, and many long ere this had borne hither the serpent's head an they could win me so lightly and with so little labor as hath fallen to thee when thou smotest the head from the dragon. An it be God's will, thou shalt not get me with bridal gift so little."

Then answered the Seneschal: "Princess Ysolt, wherefore will ye so hold against me, speaking angerly unto me? Let now the King answer first, and he must give us fairer answer and more seemly.

For sikerly he must accomplish my desire both touching you and the realm, as behoveth him honorably to do. But ye do not after the manner beseemeth you, for never will ye love them that love you. Such certes is the usage of women alway, to missay and rebuke them that love them and to show friendship unto their foes. Alway a woman hateth her lover and longeth unto him that she may not have and striveth unto that she may not bring to pass and forsaketh such as she ought to love. Now insomuch as I have so long and eagerly loved and desired you, your heart turneth altogether from me, and here openly ye revile me unto your power for to deny and rob me of the glory that I won with my hardihood and right valiant maistries. But wit ye well when I slew the dragon ye durst not have come there for all this realm, and so had ye been afeard, ye had well waxen wood to see the stiff debate and grim battle that I wrought with the dragon, and had the better."

Then said the Princess Ysolt: "Yé say sooth, surely I might not endure for all the gold and treasure of this kingdom to see you slay the dragon: and I were wretched overmuch if I desired all that I might, and loved all that would love me. But little ye know my nature sith ye say that I forsake that I would have. Whiles I eat my meat, and whiles I eat it not, because me list eat some meats but not all. Then only I eat my meat when it beseemeth me, but not when it shameth and annoyeth me. Ye would fain have me, but never would I have you nor no king's gift, and never shall ye have me for any services whatever that ye have done. Howbeit for the sake of your much wisdom and the deeds ye say ye have done, a boon shall yet be given you the which befitteth you. It is said here in the King's court that another slew the dragon and not ye, and ye have thought to have the guerdon of another's prowess. But the day ye thought to have it shall ye never live nor have joy of it."

Then said the Seneschal: "Teach me now who be they that speak thus, for there is no man in all the kingdom may say more truly than I that he fordid the dragon. But if one be found that will otherwise say, then will I prove it upon him in arms and combat that he hath spoken a lie."

Chapter xlii

TRISTRAM abode now hearkening for the speech of Ysolt, and understood that she would no more answer the Seneschal, and he began his speech boldly and spake with clear words afore all the nobles and gentlemen that were there:

"Hearken now, Sir Seneschal. Ye say ye have slain the dragon because that ye benome him his head: but sikerly it shall be shown that another was there ere that ye came. Here am I ready to maintain it. If ye dare withsay it, ye shall defend the same an ye be hardy, and it shall well be tried how truthful ye be, and it shall be shown that I slew the serpent and that with wrong crave ye a boon of the King. This am I ready for to defend with my weapons against your false demands after such fashion as the King shall ordain and the court shall devise and the wisest men shall judge."

Then spake the King: "Ensure ye the combat betwixt you by handfasting, and give us pledges and sureties that what is now assigned will be kept."

Then Tristram betaught unto the King his glove in pledge, and therewith the King spake: "I make charge against him, and the merchants of Flanders, his fellows, must forthwith set him free."

Then sprang up a score fellows unto Tristram, and each of them was a knight right valiant, fair and well armed, and said: "My lord the King, we be sureties for this our fellow, and thereto all our goods and gear."

Anon spake the King: "My lady the Queen, I put in your governance and power this man: if he faileth and dareth not to hold his foreward, I will take his body from you, for he shall surely defend this charge."

Then said the Queen: "I will guard him as worthily as me beseemeth in our chamber, with God's keeping and honorable entertainment and safe peace, in such wise that no man durst offend him."

Now have they given their pledges both, and set sureties and appointed a day unto the combat. And Tristram abode in the Queen's chambers, and baths and ointments were given him, and with mickle care

TRISTRAM OFFERETH

HIS GAGE TO GORMON

was he guarded, and worthily honored, and what that ever he required was given him.

Chapter xliii

ON a day that he sat in the bath that was carefully prepared for him with divers healing herbs for to draw the pain from all his limbs, the Princess Ysolt came to have speech with him, and she looked upon his fair visage with loving eyes and mused and said:

"If this man have valor accordant to his bigness, then may he well defend him against any single man, and well meseemeth he hath strength sufficient unto a stern fight, for knightly is he shapen." Then she yode unto his arms and beheld them, and when she saw his hose of mail and his hauberk, she said: "Passing good is this harness, and this helm will not fail." And she went unto his sword and set hand to the hilt and said: "This sword is long, and if a mighty man hold it, sore buffets will he smite with the same, and death upon what man standeth against him. These be all good arms for to maintain peace for buying and selling: and this sword is the most fairest, an the blade be not false or consumed in the venom of the dragon."

And sith she had a fantasy to see the sword, she drew it forth, and espied forthwithal the breach was made what time Tristram slew Morhaut: and much it troubled her mind in what deed that breach was made in the sword, and it seemed her it might never have been done in the dragon slaying, rather that it was already there. Then went she unto her coffer, and took thence the piece of the sword she there kept, and set it in the breach, and it fell into place as it had right then sprung forth. When she perceived it fit so cleanly the sword, she made heartly dole and began therewith to quake with rage and anger, and she sweated over her whole body with the hate and wrath that stirred and enchafed her.

"This churl," said she, "he hath slain my mother's brother. If I slay him not with this sword, then am I wretch and unworthy, an I destroy not his life and make me joy of his death."

And forthwith she went with that broken sword thereas he sat in the bath and brandished the sword over his head and said unto him:

"Thou foul churl, for the sake of mine eme, the which thou durst slay, shalt thou die. Never man shall trust thee more, though long thou hast concealed thee. Wit thou well that now suddenly in this place thou shalt die and with this sword will I thee destroy. Naught shall do thee boot." And she brandished the sword again.

Then ran he straightway unto the Princess and said: "Mercy, mercy! Let me speak but three words ere thou slay me. Do then as thee list to do. Twice hast thou given me life and from a twofold death hast thou delivered me. Erst mightest thou guiltless have slain me: but rather thou healedst me when I was nigh unto death for the wound that I took of the poisoned sword, what time I taught thee harping: now again hast thou saved me my life. Now certes is it in thy power to slay me here in this bath. But thou knowest I am thy hostage and ordained to do battle to defend thine honor, and nowise is it courteous nor seemly for a woman, neither a glory nor a joy for to slay me. Gentle maiden and fair, to what end didst thou me heal an thou wouldst now destroy me, healed and whole? All that for me thou hast suffered is straightway lost when that thou seest me die, and thereby will thy friends be no more than now. Fair Ysolt," said he, "bethink thee that I am pledged unto thy father, given as hostage to thee and thy mother. If thou slay me, natheless must thy mother yield me up unto the King as himself hath appointed."

When Ysolt heard how he named the day assigned unto the combat he had undernome against the Seneschal, then she bethought her how she hated above any man living the Seneschal, the which would possess her malgre her head, and she looked upon Tristram, the which should defend her. Then she drew toward her the sword and would not smite him, and she wept sore and sighed with all her heart, of her wrath and her misery. Natheless her womanly nature withheld the sword for to spare him. What time she waxed wroth, she brandished the sword, but when she remembered her of the Seneschal, her heat vanished.

Chapter xliv

THEN came the Queen Ysolt and when she beheld her daughter and the sword in her hand, she said:

"Are ye out of your wit? What accusation make ye against this merchant?" And right so she begripped her arm and took from her the sword.

Then said the Princess Ysolt: "Ah mother, this man slew your brother, Morhaut."

When her mother understood what the damozel said, she ran straight unto Tristram and would cut him down. But the Princess Ysolt leapt unto her forthwith and held her. Then said the Queen:

"Flee away. I will avenge my brother."

Then spake the Princess Ysolt: "Yield me the sword. I will avenge Morhaut, for better may I, which am not sworn, slay him: but he is your ward and is set in your keeping for his safety. Ye are promised to bring him unto the King, whole and well guarded, and therefore it beseemeth you slay him not."

Then each hindered other so that the Queen performed not her brother's vengeance. Neither would let go the sword, and thereby was the vengeance hindered and tarried. Tristram was afeard and besought her of pity and mercy for his life.

"Fair Queen," said he, "have pity of me."

So spake he much with meekness and soft speech, and oft he begged mercy so that at the last neither of them would slay him. Then sent they for the King, and when he was come, they fell at his feet.

"Lord," said they, "grant us a boon we would require at thee."

"Right gladly," said the King, "if it beseemeth me to grant it."

"Hither is comen," said the Queen, "that Tristram which slew my brother. But now whereas he hath also slain the dragon, I require thee that thou forgive the death of Morhaut on this condition that he free our realm and our daughter from the slander and the wickedness of the Seneschal as he hath behoten us."

"Sith that I have granted your boon and thou hast endured more than I, and sith ye will both forgive him Morhaut's death, and none hath endured more in this than thou, I will even do as best liketh thee."

Then Tristram fell at the King's feet and yielded him thanks, and the Princess Ysolt and the Queen raised him up. Then said he unto the King:

"Hearken, my lord the King. The courteous and mighty Mark, King over England, sendeth you his message that ye give him Ysolt, your daughter. And if ye will know the sooth and make peace on this condition, then shall she possess in bridal-gift all Cornwall and be lady over all England. Better land is there none in the whole world, nor men more gentle. Earls and barons will do her homage, and so shall she be of all England Queen. Therefore, beseemeth well your honor thus to be accorded, and to both realms, England and Ireland, will it be peace and joy."

When the King heard this message, he said unto Tristram: "Ensure me now that this covenant shall be held, and I will that your fellows also do in like wise that no treason may lurk hereunder, and then will I send with you unto the King, your eme, the Princess Ysolt, my daughter."

Therewithal the King let bear in hallows, and Tristram made oath that this covenant should be held on the King's half of England.

Chapter xlv

NOW came the day prefixed that was set for the earls and barons of the King's court to behold the battle that Tristram and the Seneschal had appointed. And the King led Tristram into the hall and spake in hearing of all:

"Now are ye all witness that faithfully have I watched my ward. Let him now come forth as was concluded and appointed."

Then said Tristram tofore all the courtiers and nobles of the King unto the Seneschal: "Hear now, thou churl: this tongue which I have here I cut from that head which lieth there when I destroyed the dragon. And anon shall it be shown in the head that thence I took the tongue, and so shall it be proved openly that I bear not lies nor falsehood afore good men and the company of courtiers. Now an ye trow me not, take then the head in hand and behold what hath befallen in the mouth thereof. Howbeit an he will not then confess that he lieth, let him go unto his arms and dress him for to defend him, for wit ye well I will give him the lie, that never he slew the dragon."

Then the King let bring afore him the dragon's head, and all they found that the tongue was carven therefrom. And every man scorned and loathed the Seneschal, and ever after was he known and shent and in little ease for that he durst bring so great lies afore the courtiers and wise men of the land. Then whiles the courtiers were still assembled in the King's palace, the King proclaimed unto all the men of Ireland his purpose that he had in mind for his daughter, to wit, that he would give her in marriage unto the king of England, and it seemed unto all the most honorable counsel, that hate and strife should be done away, and peace and freedom be held and stablished betwixt Ireland and England.

Chapter xlvi

THEREUPON was purveyed richly the journey of the damozel and Tristram. And the Queen made cunningly a secret drink of divers flowers and herbs with marvelous crafts, and made it so likerous of power that no man living that drank thereof might withhold him of loving the woman that drank thereof with him as long as he lived. Thereafter the Queen put this drink in a little flacket, and spake with the maiden that should be gentlewoman unto the Princess Ysolt, the which hight Bringvain:

"Bringvain, heed well this flacket. Thou shalt go with my daughter, and the first night that they, the King and she, lie together and he craveth wine, give unto them both this drink."

Then answered Bringvain: "I will well as ye have commanded me."

And they repaired, all garnished, unto the ship: and the King and Queen went with their daughter unto the ship, and the tide rose. Then many wept, men and women, that were nurtured nigh the Princess, for she was held in great love and was dear unto every man for her courtesy and meekness. When the Princess Ysolt was arrived on the ship, they drew up sail, and took the sea with the straightest wind. The damsel wept and complained of that she had lost her kin and friends and country and most loving father and mother for the sake of an unknown man. And such fortune liked her ill, and she sighed from her whole heart and said:

"Far liefer had I been dead than I had journeyed hither."

But Tristram recomforted her with much mirth. And now Tristram sailed on and the weather was fair, and because the sun's heat was burning he thirsted much, and he craved wine for to drink. And right so springeth up a certain squire that longed unto Tristram, and filleth a goblet from the flacket the Queen had betaught Bringvain to keep. And

TRISTRAM OFFERETH THE GOBLET TO YSOLT

whenas Tristram taketh the goblet 'he drinketh the
half, and letteth the Princess drink that remaineth
in the goblet. Now are they both betrayed by the
drink that they have drunk, for the squire hath
erred. And thereof cometh unto them both dolorous life and torment and long travail with desire
of the body and jeopardy of love. Forthwithal is
Tristram's desire set upon Ysolt, and her desire all
wholly upon him with such fierce longing that no
remedy may they use against it. Now sail they with
all sails filled and make a straight course unto England: and within a while the knights say they see
land rising up from the sea, and all are blithe but
only Tristram, the which was fulfilled of love, for
if it might be so as him list, then would they never
behold land, but liefer would he turn him out to
the seaward with his love and desire and delight.
But natheless, they sailed on unto the land, and
made landage in a good haven: and men knew
Tristram's ship, and a young man leapt upon a swift
horse, and rode unto the King, and found him in
the forest on hunting, and said unto him:

"Lord, we have seen Tristram's ship arrive in
the haven."

When the King heard these tidings he was blithe
and right glad and forthwith he made the young
man knight, and gave him good arms for the sake
of his joyous tidings. Then the King rode down
unto the strand. Thereafter he sent a summons over
all his realm, and held his wedding with Ysolt with
great honor and kingly worship, and solaced him

that day and all those that were there with great joyance. But the Lady Ysolt was the most woefulest woman: and when the evening came, she took Tristram by the hand, and they went together to the King's sleeping chamber, and called unto them Bringvain, her gentlewoman, for privy speech. And Ysolt began to weep sore and prayed her with fair words that she should help her that night, and be in the Queen's stead in the King's palace and in his bed, for she wist Bringvain was a virgin maid, and she herself was not. So long they besought the maiden with caresses and fair words that she granted unto their prayer, and clothed her in all the Queen's robes like as she had been the Queen; and she went in the stead of her mistress unto the King's bed, and the Queen was in Bringvain's raiment. Now the King was glad and merry and somewhat drunken when he went unto his bed, and Tristram quenched anon the lights of all the candlesticks, and the King took Bringvain in his arms and disported him with her. But Ysolt was 'heavy and doubted that Bringvain should betray her and discover unto the King what was betid, and for that cause she put her right close unto them that night for to wit what they spake. But when the King slept, Bringvain avoided and the Queen lay down by the King. When he awoke, he craved wine to drink, and Bringvain with subtlety gave him of that wine that the Queen of Ireland mingled, but the Queen drank not thereof at that time. After a space the King turned him unto her and slept by her so that he apperceived not that she was not the same: and because that he found her in all thing meek and pleasing, he showed her so much love and joy and mirth that Ysolt was right blithe. They spake then all manner of mirths as beseemed their youth, with kingly delight and queenly worship. So fared the night with them in loving pleasaunce. And thereafter Ysolt made her glad and blithe and beloved of the King and honored and worthied of all, rich and poor. And Tristram and she met together privily what time they might, and because that she was ever in his ward it came in no man's thought to have suspicion at them.

Chapter xlvii

ON a day when the Queen sat in her array, it came into her thought how that no man living wist her dealings and Tristram's save Bringvain only, her gentlewoman: and she mused then and misdoubted that Bringvain should not wish to be true to her in this secret matter and might wish to do it away and tell the King, and her evil will might come to the point that she should betray her: and if it so befell that by fortune she revealed their loves, then she knew that she would be slandered and Tristram hated and missaid. She weened then that if Bringvain were dead, she need no man fear to betray her, and she called unto her two thralls of the King and said unto them:

"Take this maiden and lead her far out into the

forest, and strike the head from her so privily that none may have knowledge thereof but me. I give you my troth that tomorn I will free you and grant you so much good that ye shall be able to live ever with honor."

"Gladly will we, lady," said they and gave her their troth.

Then she let call unto her her gentlewoman Bringvain, and said unto her: "My fairest friend, within my heart the sorrow of my spirit so tormenteth me, and full sick have I been. Go now unto the forest with these varlets: they have knowledge where all manner of herbs are, and bring me such as thou knowest I be wont to have for plasters, that I may draw therewith the poison from the bones of men, and minish my heart's heaviness. These varlets will go with thee into the forest."

Bringvain said: "Gladly, my lady, will I go as thou sayest, for full doleful am I of thy sickness. And if God will, then will this malady harm thee not."

So went she with the thralls till that they came unto the wood that was right thickly grown; and the thralls went, the one afore and the other behind her. Therewithal he that went afore drew his sword. Then began Bringvain to shake and to have fear and dread as much as she might, and set her hands together and bade the thrall for God's sake to tell her for what trespass or by what power she should be slain. Then answered the thrall:

"That will I not hide from thee, but when thou

hast heard it straightway will I smite thee with this sword. What hast thou mischiefed Queen Ysolt that she willeth thy death? She causeth thee to be slain."

When Bringvain heard this, she said: "Mercy, for God's sake. Let me speak somewhat with you ere ye slay me, for I would send a word unto my lady, Queen Ysolt. When ye have slain me, I bid you for God's sake that ye tell her cleanly that never did I harm her. But when we journeyed hither from Ireland, we had two smocks of silk, white as snow, and her mother did on her smock or ever they were sundered. And since I was a poor maiden and hired unto unknown folk, while I was on ship, I kept my smock unto my best knowledge. But when Ysolt, my lady, came on that ship, there arose great heat of the sun that she endured not to wear her furred gown for the warmth, and she used much her good smock, day and night, that it waxed dark of her sweat. So when we were comen hither and she went unto the King's bed as Queen, and her smock was not so white as she would have it, in her great need she besought me oft of my smock to do on her, and I lent it unto her. And I wot afore God that never have I misdone her, unless she hath liked this ill and will have my death for this misdeed. Never have I known none other ill thought, anger or wrath, guilt or sin betwixt us. Now yield her God's greeting and mine, and say that I thank her of the many honors she hath done me and her bounties in this long time sith my childhood until

this day. Even as for this my death I forgive it
her. And now in God's name strike so soon as thou
wilt."

Chapter xlviii

WHENAS the thrall heard her word and her
piteous weeping and wist that she had done
no greater wrong unto the Queen, they made her
large excuse and found in her no blame and they
bound her till a great tree. Then they caught a
great hare and slew it and cut out the tongue and
yode home and came afore the Queen and she asked
of them privily what they had done. Then one of
them took forth the tongue and showed it unto her
and said:

"My lady, we slew her and have brought home
the tongue."

Then Queen Ysolt asked what she said ere she
died, and the thralls told the Queen her greeting
and all else that she had said.

"Cease," said she, "ye shall not say so." And
the Queen cried with a loud voice: "Ye vile thralls,
why have ye slain my gentlewoman? I will wreak
her death upon you and your bodies, and will let
horses tear you in sunder or burn you on the pyre,
an ye give me not again, whole and unharmed, her
that I betaught you to guide into the wood. But I
give you my troth that if ye bring her unto me again
I will free you both."

Then said the other thrall: "Mercy, my lady. Fickle is your mind. All was otherwise that ye spake yesterday when ye bade us slay her and that so should we be freed. But now will ye fordo us for her sake. But if we had refused what ye bade us do, then had death been prepared for us forthwith."

Then said the Queen: "Thou son of a whore, bring me hither the damozel forthwith: this day will I free thee."

Then answered the other thrall: "God you thank, my lady. Bringvain, your handmaid, yet liveth: I will bring her unto you whole and safe."

So the Queen suffered one thrall to go after Bringvain, but one she let guard. And he that went forth straightway loosed the damozel in the forest, and led her straightway home unto the Queen's chamber. When Queen Ysolt beheld her, right so her grief turned unto joy, and she went forthwith to meet her and kissed her more than a score of times.

Chapter xlix

NOW hath Ysolt essayed Bringvain, her gentlewoman, and found her wise and courteous, and it came to pass that their love and friendship was renewed betwixt them. The Queen hath now all that pleaseth her bodily desire, daily pleasaunce of Tristram, her lover. The King showeth her love openly and Tristram secretly, for he and the Queen may do what they will within the court sith he is chief councilor unto the Queen; and all their devising was accorded with craft and secrecy so that none was ware save Bringvain neither of their words nor works, their disport and pleasaunce and mirth. No man they heard speak of their loves nor have suspicion unto them, for Tristram served her in seemly wise as the King's nephew, and well it seemed unto all that it sorted with the King's kinsman. But when they might not attain that they desired, then were they sorrowful. So they heeded their loves that never was it by either of them shamed, secretly or openly.

Tristram was hardy, debonair, and approved in knighthood. On a day he was gone on hunting, and in the mean while landed a great ship and a fair, and on this ship was a baron of Ireland the which owed the ship and was chief of all those that were in Ireland, and he was a man passing orgulous and proud. He came unto King Mark's court on a horse fair and well arrayed, and he had under his cloak a harp all dight with gold. He saluted the King and Queen Ysolt: he knew her straightway, for long had he been enamoured of her, and for her sake he came unto the King's court. When the Queen knew him, she told the King forthwith who he was and whence he came, and she bade the King do him honor and worship. The King did so and caused him to eat of his own dish. He said he was a minstrel and therefore he let hang his harp nigh him, for at no cost would he lay it down for no man's friendship or honor. When the King had eaten and the board was removed, the court made joy and cheer. Then the King asked in hearing of all his court if the Irish baron knew aught of harping, and if he would play the King a lay for love. Then answered the man of Ireland that he would delight no King in none other realm but if he wist what boon he should have therefor. Then said the King:

"Delight us now with an Irish lay, and ye shall have whatsomever ye list."

He assented him thereto and drew forth his harp and played an Irish lay that was right pleasant unto all. Then said the King that he should play them another lay as good or better, and he did them another better by half so that it rejoiced them to listen. And he said unto the King in hearing of all the court that the King should hold his foreward that was spoken and he himself should choose his reward.

"That shall be done," said the King; "tell me what ye desire."

Then answered the man of Ireland: "Ysolt shall ye yield me, for ye possess no treasure nor none other thing that I would liefer have."

The King answered: "By my faith, her shall ye never get. Ask rather some thing that ye may obtain."

He answered the King: "Now ye lie and break your promise that ye gave me in hearing of your whole court, and it is law and right that ye never more rule realm, for prince that openly lieth and forsaketh his oath and word ought never to have power nor rule over brave men. And if ye deny this that ye have spoken, then I lay it before the judgment of faithful men. And if ye find any man that will not grant me this thing and dareth contrary me, then will I defend my speech against him this day in sight of all your court, to wit, that ye promised me my will, whatsomever it was, that I would require of you. Now if ye deny me that ye promised me, ye have none right in this kingdom, and that will I prove upon you with my weapons if this your court will judge with right, and these brave men will hold their faith."

Chapter l

NOW hath King Mark hearkened his word, and he beheld his company over all the benches, and found that no man in his court durst reply nor make good his speech nor deliver his Queen: for all wist that the Irish knight was a fierce man and right stout in battle and in all manner deeds. Whenas the King saw that no man would fight against him, he betaught his wife into his power even as his councilors and his knights adjudged. And the man of Ireland took her straightway with joy and rode down unto the strand: grievous now was her sorrow that she lamented her estate and wept and lamented and sighed sore. She cursed the day that her lover went to the chase for had he been there when she was given up, he had ransomed her with stiff battle, and well she deemed he would first have given his life ere he lost her. The man of Ireland bare her now weeping unto his pavilion, and when she was laid in bed, he commanded that the ship should be readied as fast as it might that they might fare away with all speed. But the ship lay on the dry sand, and though the tide began to rise, yet was it far from the dromond.

Right so came Tristram from the wood, and tidings were given him that Ysolt the Queen was ravished away and delivered up. Then he called unto him his squire, and took his rote and leapt on his destrier, and rode as fast as he might down to the pavilion. When he came unto a hill nigh unto the pavilion, he alight from his horse and put it in the keeping of his squire to watch, and went with his rote as fast as he might to the pavilion, and he saw Ysolt lying in the embrace of this baron, weeping and sore distressed. When the man of Ireland saw the minstrel as he came unto the pavilion, he said:

"Fellow, play us a fair lay on thy rote, and I will give thee a mantle and a good robe if thou canst solace my lady."

Then said Tristram: "God you thank. I will do so much that she will not mourn this year if I set my mind to divert her."

Now he made ready his rote and made them good disport with a fair song. Ysolt hearkened through the night and was solaced by the coming of her friend and lover. When he had ended his playing, the dromond was afloat, and then said a man of Ireland unto this baron:

"Lord, let us depart with all the speed we may: ye dwell here all too long. An lord Tristram came home from hunting, then it were to fear that he would hinder somewhat our voyage. He is famous above all the knights that be in this realm, and he is chief of them all."

Then said that lord: "Fie upon them that fear his assault. Friend," quoth he, "play me now other lays to rejoice withal Ysolt my lady so that thou drive her sorrow from her."

Tristram accorded then his rote and sang a matchless song and wondrous to hear that treated of love; and Ysolt listened thereto with all her heart. Long he made the playing, and he ended it with sadness. In the mean while the tide had so flowed that one might not come to the bridge, and the bridge stood under water nigh the ship. Then said the man of Ireland:

"What now shall we do? How shall we bring Ysolt to the board? Let now the sea ebb till she may come to the bridge with dry foot."

Tristram said: "I have a good horse in the valley nigh hand."

"Do me this grace," said the baron, "and bring hither the horse."

Tristram came anon unto his horse and leapt on his back and took his sword and came riding therewith to the baron of Ireland.

"Lord," said he, "give me here the lady Ysolt. I promise you I will deal courteously with her."

And the man of Ireland lift her up into the saddle and bade him with fair words that he deal well and courteously with her. When now Tristram had gotten Ysolt again, he cried on high:

"Hear, thou fool and heedless. Thou wonnest Ysolt with thy harp, but thou hast lost her by reason of a rote. Meet is it thou shouldst lose her, for with treason thou wonnest her. Go again shamed and dishonored to Ireland, thou foul traitor. With craft thou hadst her of the King, and with craft have I her again from thee."

Right so he smote his horse with the spurs, and rode swiftly up the sands, and so into the wood. Now sikerly hath the man of Ireland lost Ysolt, for Tristram hath borne away his love. And when evening fell, they were in the wood, and they purveyed for them as best they might, and they dwelt there that night in love and peace. On the morrow when day came, he rode home with her to the King's court and gave her up to the King and said:

"Lord, by the faith of my body, little it behoveth a woman love a man that giveth her up for one harping only. Now keep her another time better for only by great cunning is she brought again."

Chapter li

TRISTRAM loved Ysolt without ceasing, and she him again as faithfully, both of them with subtlety and seemliness: so great was the power of their loves as it had been that they were of one mind and one heart, until that men spake of it and others had wonder of it: but then was there no man that wist in certain, but it was noised only on suspicion. Tristram had a fellow, the which he loved right well with all good faith and fair fellowship, and he was the Seneschal and nigh unto the King, so that he took counsel with him of all thing that he would do, and he hight Meriadoc by name. They were ever together, Tristram and he, and had both one chamber. It happed on a night they slept both together: and whenas the Seneschal was fallen on sleep in bed, Tristram stole forth from him, and when he went out the snow was fallen, and the moon shone as bright as it were day. When he came to the palings of the orchard, he pulled out a board where he was wont to go in. And there Bringvain took him by the hand and led him unto the lady Ysolt, and took an ash-basket and turned it upso down over the candles that the light of the candles might not reach them. Then she went unto her bed and forgat to close the door, and Tristram played him with the Queen.

In the meanwhile the Seneschal dreamed a dream

that he thought he saw come out of the forest a boar right huge, with gaping mouth and his teeth whetted as he were wood, and so horrible in semblaunt as he would tear any thing in pieces: and he took his way into the castle; and when he came there, there was no man in the King's court durst go afore him nor meet him nor abide him. And he saw that he rushed at the King's bed and struck the King betwixt the shoulders so that from the blood and foam that dripped from his mouth he defiled the bedclothing: and then came a great folk to help the King, but he durst do naught against him. Then Meriadoc woke from weariness and grief of the dream, and thought at first it was true, and then it came into his mind that it was a dream, and it seemed him marvelous what it should signify, and he called unto Tristram, his fellow, and would tell him these tidings. So he groped and would tell him the dream, seeking him, but found him nowhere. Then he arose and went to the door and found it open, and he thought then that Tristram was gone to disport him this night, and it seemed him strange he should go out so privily that no man took note of his departure and he should tell no man whither he would go. And Meriadoc espied afore him in the snow his tracks and he put on his shoes and followed his path, for the moon gave him light sufficient, and when he was come to the orchard he found straightway the opening there Tristram had entered. He marveled where he was gone, for he had no suspicion at the Queen, rather he deemed he was a lover of the Queen's gentlewoman, and he went forward and entered secretly and as silently as he might for to espy what was betid, so that at the last he heard their speech, Tristram's and the Queen's. He doubted what he should do, and his mind was all astonied, and ill it liked him to endure such shame and damage of the King; but he durst not speak forth, for he feared to slander them. Then he turned him again by the same path that night. He made as that he wist naught of the matter. When Tristram returned, he lay down in his bed beside him, and neither spake with other. This was the first chance by which their love was published; for never was no man ware of it afore, neither by night nor by day. Thus it dured so long that they that were jealous and enemies unto Tristram did King Mark to wit of their secret case: and now came upon the King sore grief and grievous sorrow and dole and misease, and he knew not what he should do, and he let spy concerning their deeds.

Chapter lii

WHEN the King thought to essay the Queen and to hear her answer, and he accused her of her untruth. On a night when the King lay in his bed beside her, he said to her with sorrowful words:

"My lady, I would be a pilgrim and seek holy places for to help me. Now I wot not into whose hands I should beteach it to watch over my court: therefore would I now hear what rede thou enjoinest or what would best ease and pleasure thee. Now tell me your advice and whose governance thou wouldst be in, and I will follow your counsel."

Ysolt said: "Strange it seemeth me that thou doubtest what would advantage thee best in that whereof thou speakest. Who should watch over me but if it be Lord Tristram? So seemeth me to behove thee best that in his keeping I should be: he can defend thy realm and watch over thy court. He is thy sister's son, and he will set all his intent that your honor and the court be maintained with faithful service and loyal governance in all peace and to the joy of all men."

When the King had heard her word and counsel, he went at the dayspringing unto the Seneschal, that willed evil unto the Queen, and told him all Ysolt's saying: and Meriadoc answered:

"So is it surely as I have heard said. Now may ye clearly discover from her language that she would be thereas it liked her best: for she loveth him so much that she may not lain it. Marvel is it ye will so long endure such shame and will not drive Tristram from you."

But the King was in great amazement, and doubted and deemed that it might be true that was told him of Ysolt and Tristram. Now when Ysolt rose from her bed, she called unto her Bringvain, her maiden, and said:

"Dearest friend, knowest thou not I have heard

good tidings and such as like me well, that the King will go into foreign countries, and in that space I shall be in the rule of my love, and we will have delight and game, whomever it mislike."

Then answered Bringvain: "How knowest thou this, or who told it unto thee?"

Then Ysolt told her what the King said. But Bringvain understood forthwith her folly and said:

"Thou knowest not to conceal, and the Seneschal hath brought this to pass that through the false speech that was set before thee and to which thou gavest trust thou hast betrayed thyself. Now have they discovered and by thine own words proved it."

And she showed her counsel and learned her an answer to answer the King for to escape from the jeopardy of those things the Seneschal put upon her.

Chapter liii

KING MARK mused much of this matter with waking and grief, and he would wit with full certain witting what it beseemed him surely to believe touching the slander that had failen upon Ysolt and Tristram. Another night as he lay in his bed beside Ysolt, he essayed again a wile and would try her. Now she lay in his embrace with much pleasaunce and sweet kisses and with such sport as most delighteth both cotters and Kings. But she perceived anon that he would try her as he had afore done, and she changed her cheer about and sighed with all her heart and wept and cursed the day she beheld him and he led her unto his bed, and said:

"Full miserable am I that was born to dole and sorrow, so ever have all things fared grievously with me. That can I least enchieve that most behoveth me, and he I would liefest have will least love me." And she showed the King woe and anguish, sorrow and heaviness, wrath and grief with many tears. Then said the King unto her:

"Fair lady, what annoyeth thee, or for what weepest thou?"

Then answered Ysolt: "Many are the causes of my sorrows and pains past enduring, but if thou allay them. Methought thou hadst been jesting of that thou spakest one night afore, or that it had been sport thou spakest of desiring to repair thee unto foreign lands. But now have I ascertained all concerning thine intent to depart. Unhappy is woman that loveth man overmuch. Never may no woman trust man sith that thou purposest to go from me and let me tarry here after thee. Sith thou hast taken this counsel, why hast thou hidden it from me? Today was it told me surely that thou wouldst depart: where wilt thou that I abide, or what friends of ours will watch over me? For thy sake left I all helpful counsel, father and mother, kindred and friends, great honors and happiness and lands. Shame and disworship is it unto thee to leave me abiding here. Never shall I win solace, night nor day, as soon as I lose thy love. For God's love, dwell at home or let me, wretch that I am, go with thee."

King Mark said: "My lady, I will not leave thee alone, for Tristram, my nephew, shall watch over thee with great tenderness and seemly service: is no man in my realm I love as him, and in special for that he serveth thee so courteously."

Ysolt said: "Right evil is my fortune that he should defend me and that in his keeping I should be. His service, love, and pleasaunce are known to me: false are they and treason though fair is his speech. So he fareth as he were my friend, for sith he slew mine uncle he speaketh me fair that I should not take vengeance of him nor hate him. But he knoweth right surely that his pleasaunce giveth me no solace for the great woe and shame and damage that he wrought me and my family; and were he not thy nephew, my lord, I had long since done him to wit my wrath and avenged on him my woe and grief and never seen nor spoken with him. But I meddle with him by reason of this charge that is laid against me through the common noise that I hate thy kindred and thy dearest friend: for it is often said that hideous may be the mind of a woman that she loveth not the kindred of her husband, and by her speech and works she will not suffer them near, night nor day. Now for this cause have I kept me from slander and evil speaking and received his pleasaunce and service. But never would I be in his power nor receive his service: rather I require of thee, my lord, that thou suffer me depart with thee."

So spake she much as at this time, and the King forgave her all his anger. Then went he unto the Seneschal and told him that no love was betwixt them, the Queen and Tristram. But the Seneschal essayed with all subtlety to teach the King what he should say unto the Queen to try her: and when the King had heard his word, he went unto the Queen and said that certainly he would depart, but she should tarry after in keeping of the noblest men and friends that should honor her with all manner honor and worship. "And I will that none shall do aught that misliketh thee nor refuse aught that is thee loth. But sith that it pleaseth thee not that Tristram, my kinsman, be in thy service, I will for the sake of thy love sunder him from thee and send him into other countries, for at no cost will I love him against thy will and honor."

Ysolt said: "Lord, never shalt thou do this wrong, for then will men say over all thy realm that I have brought thee unto such purpose, and that I hate thy kindred because of Morhaut's death, and put thee on to hate him to the end that I would rob him of the governance of thy realm. But he is most bound unto thee and truest for to defend thee, and for this cause shall I be defamed, and I will not that thou hate thy kinsman for my love. It be-seemeth thee not to cause him depart for my sake nor to leave thy realm and peace and protection. But I am a woman and if war ariseth, thy foes will hastily take thy realm from me, for I have not strength nor might to defend it: and it will be said that I purchased Tristram's going for that he was the strongest defense of our realm, and that I hated him so much that he might not remain afore me. Now do either of two things: that I go with thee forthwith, or give him the rule and defense of our kingdom."

The King hearkened closely unto the words of Ysolt, and he discovered that she had much goodwill unto Tristram, and he had the same suspicion, and he suffered great woe and dolor, and his wrath and heaviness were renewed. But on the morn the Queen went to have speech with Bringvain, and she called her a fool and of little wit, and told her then a good device, how she should answer the King touching his purpose to send Tristram away.

Chapter liv

THEREAFTER the King would that Tristram be no more within the court by reason of the slander that had fallen on Tristram and the Queen, and he carefully departed them, and Tristram dwelt now in a town beneath the castle, and he purveyed him there a lodging and with great dispense, but now was he ever sorrowful and Ysolt also that they might not come together. Now because they were parted in sunder, each of them waxed pale for sor-

row and longing, for they have lost their loves: and
the whole court now perceived their malease and
the King perceived it clearly and he bethought him
of a subtle craft, for he wist that gladly would they
come together for the sorrow and heaviness they
endured of their departition because they were so
straightly watched. On a day the King sent for his
hounds and let make ready his horse and sent men
forth into the forest to set up lodges and pitch pavilions, and let stuff them with wine and meats, for
he said he would stay on hunting six weeks or more.
And then he took leave at the Queen to go and disport him, and went into the forest. When Tristram
heard of the King's departing, then was his mind
eased, and he gave it out that he was sick and tarried at home to try if some chance should be when
he might meet the Queen. Then he took a wand
and cut thereof fair chips so cunningly that no man
had seen their like, for when they were cast on the
water they sank not but floated on the water as it
had been foam, and no stream might hurt them.
And what time Tristram would have speech with
Ysolt, he threw the chips in the brook that ran nigh
her bower and before the Queen's chamber; and
the Queen wist straightway and perceived by this
craft his will and presence. When Tristram stood
and cut the wand, a dwarf came forth of the castle
and said:

"The greeting of God and the Lady Ysolt. She
sendeth you word that she would speak with you.
Now fail not at no cost to come unto her where last

ye found her, and I trust that ye will remember the place. I tell you alone privily. It is not concluded whether it will again betide as it hath now chanced, for all the court is gone forth on hunting, and therefore she sendeth you word to come at night to speak with her. Now tell me the words ye will send her, for I dare tarry here no longer because of the evil men that envy me and tell the King that I do all the evil that is betwixt you. An they wist I were here, they would defame me and accuse me before the King."

Tristram said unto him: "Friend, God thank thee that thou art willing to bear me messages, and it shall be to thy profit an I live. But as at this time, though it be little, I give thee my mantle with white fur, and another time it shall be more. Now I bid thee for my love thou say that unto the right gentle Ysolt I send God's greeting and my friendship, and tell her that I may not come for there is a great pain in my head and all this night was I sore sick. But tomorn, if I may by any mean, I will go to see her if she seeketh aught of me, and then may she say whatso she desireth."

The dwarf then took leave and went home unto the castle whereas the King had hidden to wait upon them, and he told the King what he had said to Tristram and how he had answered.

"Sir King, Tristram hideth all afore me. But certes this night will ye see and discover all their cheer that long in secret they have been wont to enjoy, for I saw him that he cut chips that he is wont to cast on the water to draw and call Ysolt unto him."

And they spake so much they found at the last the rede and device that the King should hide him that night and watch their tryst thereas they were wont to come together.

Chapter lv

WHEN evening was come, Tristram made ready and went unto the brook nigh the orchard, for Ysolt used to sit there beside the brook each evening a space to comfort her and lament the days of her youth. And when she was come thither, she espied the chips floating, and she understood that Tristram was already come unto the orchard, and she hilled herself all in her mantle that was of white fur, and she hied her with her head covered into the garden under the tree, wherein the King sat already. But Tristram came another way across the garden and went unto the tree where their custom was to meet. But right at that point the moon arose and shone brightly. Then he beheld the shadow of the King on the earth, and he stood still for he apperceived that the King would spy on them. Much he grieved and feared for the Queen that she might not perceive the shadow. But therewith she saw the shadow and made countenance as she were araged against Tristram and spake much evil of him. Then they went away both, and they understood that they were betrayed in this dolorous and woeful matter. But the King tarried under the tree and was loth to believe yet this accusation, and therefore he gave up his wrath against them both. So was it till a day that they were leten blood, the King, the Queen, and Tristram, for the King would now essay them privily in his chamber, and Tristram had not noted his subtlety. And in the night, when all were on sleep, the King let no man abide there save only Tristram.

"Nephew," said the King, "quench all our candles. They are noyous unto me with their shining."

And he spake so, for cause that he had long studied a great craft and sleight after the counsel of his evil dwarf, the which ever conceived malice against Ysolt and Tristram. So that evil dwarf rose up secretly from his bed and took a basket that he had by his bed filled with flour and strewed it over all the floor that he might espy Tristram's footprints in the flour an he should go unto the Queen. But right so Bringvain was ware what he did and showed it unto Tristram. Then arose the King in the middes of the night and said he was weary of lying and would go unto matinsong and bade the dwarf follow him. When now the King was departed and Tristram lay still, then he cast how he might come at the Queen, for he wist that if he walked unto her, his footprints might be seen in the flour: therefore with both feet he leapt over the flour to the Queen's bed. And he was so faint of that leap that his veins opened and bled all night. When he arose, he leapt again into his bed. Then came the King and saw that blood was on her bed, and he asked Ysolt whence that blood came. She said that her hand bled. Then the King went unto Tristram's bed and saw him bloody, and he understood that Ysolt lied. Then came upon him an open suspicion, but wroth was he and woe, for he wist naught was proved save of the blood that he saw, and that was not certain accusation nor trusty tokening. And for this cause was the King in doubt and knew not what he should believe: for he might not with no sure token pardon them, and yet would he nowise give up; rather would he publish this thing, yet would he not accuse them. Then he sent for all his barons and councilors, and he made complaint of his woe for Ysolt and Tristram, and all his barons spake of this matter and gladly they would punish them if sure proofs might be found.

Chapter lvi

THEN the King sent for all his councilors unto London, and all came thither that would have the King's friendship, bishops and barons and all the wisest men that were in England. And when they were comen there, the King prayed them to set before him a sure devising how he might conclude this matter against Tristram and Ysolt, that had brought so great slander upon him that he was defamed over all his realm. Then said the King's councilors, some folly and others wisdom and understanding. Thereupon stood up an ancient bishop and said unto the King:

"Lord, hearken to what I shall say, and if I speak thing that is right, then assent ye thereto. There be many men in our land that make accusation against Tristram that dare not prove it against him. Thou requirest us of counsel, lord King, and it behoveth us all give thee siker counsel, true and trustworthy. Beseemeth thee not endure this slander, yet mayest thou not put upon them open accusation, for thou hast not found them with the deed so that thou mayest not manifestly show their guilt. With what jeopardy shouldst thou condemn thy sister's son and own wife? for ye twain be lawfully wedded, and ye may not by no mean be severed in such case when she may not be discovered in no open guilt, whereof her enemies and malicious men accuse her. But in like wise it beseemeth thee not to forbear of this because of the blame and noise that the folk troweth and speaketh of, whether it be right or false: for ofttimes men believe no less falsehood than truth. But because of this slander thou hast so meekly borne and for that thou hast accused the Queen of this shame, beseemeth thee well that she come hither by summons before these courtiers, and hear ye then my speech and her answer: and when she hath answered, then shall we have it by rightwise judgment that she shall not sleep in the King's bed but if she have cast this slander from her."

Then answered the King: "Unto this judgment I assent me gladly, here afore all the courtiers and lords."

Therewithal they sent for Ysolt, and she came forthwith at their summons into the hall and sat down. Then the bishop stood up and said unto her:

"Queen, hearken what the King hath bidden me tell thee. It is known now to all men, within the court and without, touching a certain slander that hath lighted generally upon thee, and better than a twelvemonth hath remained, touching thee and Tristram, our King's nephew. And be it true or false, there resteth on thee open slander and accusation and treason unto the King. But he hath not seen openly nor discovered aught but good, but only this slander that men speak of, and that with no sure tokening of your deeds. Now before these courtiers and lords, I appeal thee of these crimes, and I require thee of a straight ordeal that thou mayest free thee and deliver the King of this annoyance, for it beseemeth thee not to have ado with the King in bed ere thou hast purged thee of this slander."

Ysolt was a woman well witted and debonair and right fair and courageous, and she stood up afore the King and said: "Good King, wit ye well that the noise that malicious and evil thoughted men put upon me is known unto me, for long ago was it said that no man liveth without slander and blame, and meseemeth no marvel that men lie against me that am blameless. It seemeth them easy, for I be a stranger and far from my kindred and friends, and

abide here in a foreign land amongst men nowise
bound unto me, like as I were a woman captived, and
I wot well that no man will pity my woe. Now
I pray the King, my lord, that he let judge my case
by ordeal afore all his court. Never may so hard
judgment be laid upon me that I will not endure it
to rescue me of the reproach of malicious men, for
I am guiltless of this slander. Let it be now the
hot iron or other ordeal: and if this ordeal misfall
me, then let the King burn me with fire or tear me
asunder with horses."

Chapter lvii

THE King hearkened Ysolt's words, that she
would fain endure the hot iron or other ordeal, and he understood that it behoved him not
demand more, for that he had found no sure proof
nor manifest guilt in her, and he must therefore
accept a rightwise judgment concerning her. Then
he said:

"Come hither now and assure me the ordeal afore
these courtiers, that this word thou hast spoken shall
be held to, for we will gladly grant it unto thee,
and thou shalt hie thee unto Caerleon, and thither I
summon you, my courtiers all, to look to my honor
and right, and we will all assemble there a month
hence."

Then came Ysolt and pledged her unto the ordeal, as the King bade. The lords then departed

and the court and went unto their homes. But Ysolt abode after with sorrow and dole, for she found now put on her the slander wherewith she was aforetime rebuked and shamed.

Chapter lviii

NOW when the day appointed was come, she bethought her of a counsel, and sent to Tristram that on the day that was assigned her he come to meet her where there was a ford and disguise himself as much as he might. She purposed that he should bear her from the boat where she was to be carried across the water, and then would she tell him a secret thing. He took good heed by his troth that he should be there nigh hand on the day assigned, all so disguised that no man knew him. His visage was all stained with yellow color, and he was in a foul woolen kirtle and an old cloak over him. The Queen on the other side of the river entered within a barge: she made a sign then unto Tristram, and anon her barge touched the other shore. Then she said on high to Tristram:

"Friend, come hither and bear me from the barge: thou shouldst be a good mariner."

Then Tristram went straightway unto the barge and took her in his arms. While he carried her, she said unto him in a low voice that he should fall upon her when he came unto the sand. When he was come from the barge a short space from the river, he fell forthwith upon her. When her men beheld that, they leapt straightway from the boat, some with staves, some with poles, some with oars, and would have beaten him to death. But the Queen gave command that they should not do him no hurt and said that it was not by his will he fell, but rather he was faint and much wearied of going, "for he is a pilgrim comen from far." And they made mirth of her words and laughed how the pilgrim fell with her, and all said she was a lady wonderly gentle that she only would not suffer to do him harm. But no man wist for what cause she had devised this counsel. Then they start on their horses and rode their ways and made jape and mockage of the pilgrim, how merrily it had betid with him.

"Now should it be a marvel," said Ysolt, "an the pilgrim list to play? Alas, now may I in no wise take mine oath that I have lain with no man save the King."

Then they rode to the King's court, and the Queen alight from her horse and so did all they that conveyed her.

Chapter lix

NOW the court was assembled, a great multitude. The King was stern and grim, fierce and eager to avenge him and to approve Ysolt with the hot iron that she should bear by reason of Tristram. Now the iron was laid in the fire and all ready:

[164]

YSOLT BECKONETH TO TRISTRAM

three bishops sacred it. Ysolt heard mass and wrought many almsdeeds so that whatsomever she possessed of gold or silver, robes or vessels, she gave great part thereof unto the poor for God's love: and in like wise to the sick and sore, the fatherless and poor widows. Then she yode barefoot, in woolen raiment, and miserable seemed her estate to all men. They all wept, high-born as well as low-born, strangers and men of that land, rich and poor, young and old, all their hearts gave much unto her. Now the hallowed relics were brought forth for her to take oath unto the ordeal, and she stood forth weeping and set her hand unto the holy relics. She heard then that the barons disputed touching the manner of her oath: some would press her hardly and trouble her, but other would help her in the oath-taking; most would follow the King that would make the oath-taking as harsh as it might be. Then said Ysolt:

"Sir King, hearken my oath. Never came no man born of woman nigh me, unhappy that I am, save thou, O King, and that tormented pilgrim that bare me from the barge and fell upon me in sight of you all. So help me God in this trial and purge me by this iron as never gat I blame or harm of other man. This I swear before God and all his saints. If I have not enough said in this oath, then add ye speedily thereto what ye will, and I will swear that also."

The King beheld Ysolt weeping and many other for her sake, rich and poor, because of her woes.

Then was his heart heavy, and he said unto Ysolt:

"I have heard, and meseemeth that naught needeth to add thereto. Bear now this hot iron, and may God so purge thee as thou hast deserved and as thou hast sworn."

"I will well," said she. And she set her hands under the iron and bare it so bravely that no man perceived cowardice nor dread in her. And God in his fair mercy granted her clean purgation and reconcilement and accord with the King, her lord and proper husband, with entire love and honor and great worship.

Chapter lx

WHEN Ysolt was now purged by the iron, she turned herself and declared that the King had dealt as a child for to hate his nephew for the Queen's cause. And the King left off his folly and repented him that he had afore had evil suspicion unto his nephew and purchased unto himself woe and misease of many fashions without necessity, and now he is void of all doubt so that his mind is wholly clean and guileless despite the malice of certain men. He deemed now that Ysolt was not guilty of the slander was put upon her and he was right blithe to recomfort her after her sorrow. All whereof he was possessed he esteemed as naught beside her love and grace. He loved her out of measure so that none other of God's creatures pleased him as much as the fair Ysolt.

[168]

Chapter lxi

BUT at the time that the mighty and worshipful Tristram departed out of the King's realm and they severed them in wrath, the King and he, Tristram took service with a duke of Wales. The Duke did him honor and worship above all his friends for his renown, his parage, and his puissance, his knighthood, right courteous cheer, and gentle conditions, and all manner deeds so that he was renowned above all other. It happed on a day Tristram sat mourning that he was come into a strange land and was far from his desire and love and longing, and he sighed oft from all his heart and lamented of his woe and distress that he was so far from her that he loved. Whenas the Duke espied it, he bade his squires bring him his plaything that he might solace Tristram's dolor wherewith he saw him to be sick in his court, for fain would he do him kindness and liking an it would pleasure him. Forthwith came the Duke's varlets with a costly cloth and spread it on the floor afore the Duke, and there came others that led unto him his dog, the which was sent unto him out of the land of faerye and was named Petit-cru. He was a beast wonderly fair that never was man born which could draw nor tell his cunning and shape, for what side soever one beheld the dog he seemed of so many colors that no man might perceive nor mark them. If one saw him before, he seemed white and black and green on the side was turned toward him: if one saw his side, then seemed he blood-red as it had been the flesh side of the skin were turned out and the hair inward, sometimes as he were of a dark brown color, and anon as he were in bright red skin: but when one saw him endlong, one could perceive his semblaunt least, for he seemed to have none color that might be discovered. He came from the isle that hight Avalon, and she that gave the dog unto the Duke was a fay. Never was a dog so big nor nobler nor fairer nor so cunning or meek of service. This dog was led forth of the Duke's squires with a gold chain from his treasurer's house. Forthwithal they took the chain from him, and when he was loose he shook himself, and the bells that were fastened about his neck rang with so fair a sound that Tristram lost all his sorrow and forgat his love, and all his mind and heart and temper were turned so that unnethe he wist whether he were himself or another. Was no man living that heard the sound of the bells that would not straightway have assuagement of his grief through all his heart, and be filled with joy and mirth and desire to have none other delight. Tristram listened eagerly unto the sound and looked clearly at the dog, and greater marvel by far seemed him the color of the dog than the sound of the bells. He took him then in his hand and felt him that he was all covered with soft hair and smooth: and he thought he should not keep his life an he gat not this dog for his lady Ysolt to disport her. But he wist not how he should enchieve this, and he made no countenance as he would fain have the dog, for the Duke held him so dear that he would never for no cause forsake him or look away from him.

Chapter lxii

NOW as the romance of Tristram maketh mention, there was in those days a giant and he dwelt in a country by the seashore, and every twelvemonth he took truage of all the realm, a tithe of the cattle, and the Duke paid him this fee every year: and now the giant was come to fetch his fee. Then was a cry made abroad of this truage over all the land for to pay unto the giant Urgan this scot: and there came barons and merchants and cottars, burghers and yeomen, each according to his livelihood, and drove their cattle to meet the giant, and it was marvel full great how many there were and what tumult and shouting they made as they drave the cattle unto him. Then Tristram inquired whence so great din came and who possessed the cattle and who should have it. The Duke told him straightway in what wise this was and how that he assented him unto the giant's tribute and all the dealing and the covenant that was made betwixt him and the giant. Then said Tristram unto the Duke:

"If I deliver you of this servage so that it shall never need you again to pay the scot unto the giant, what will ye give me in reward?"

The Duke said: "Whatsoever liketh you or that

[171]

ye will choose. Naught that I have is so precious
unto me that I would not give it you in guerdon if
ye rid us of this bondage."

"An ye grant me this boon," said Tristram, "I
will free you and your realm and destroy the giant
from you and the scot from your men, and make
all your land free so that it shall never more be
aggrieved."

Then said the Duke: "I grant your boon gladly
and I will swear to you this promise afore all my
court that is now here."

Tristram dressed him forthwith and armed him
and mounted his horse and said unto the Duke: "Let
some man lead me thither unto the way the giant
will pass, and I will free you and your realm of the
giant."

"God reward you!" said the Duke, and he let his
man lead him as far as a bridge where the giant
should cross over to drive the cattle. And when
Tristram was comen unto the bridge, he hindered
the cattle that they should not cross over the bridge.
When the giant beheld how that the cattle stood
still, he brandished his club of iron, and ran with
all the speed he might and saw Tristram sitting
armed upon his horse, and he shouted unto him with
a dreadful voice:

"Who art thou, caitiff, that lettest my cattle for
to pass? I swear to thee by my head that thou shalt
buy this dearly save by my mercy."

Then Tristram was wroth and said unto him:
"Never shall I conceal my name for such a cursed

fiend as thou art: the court clepeth me Tristram. Thee I fear not nor thine iron club. Thou takest this cattle with wrong, and therefore thou shalt nowise keep them longer. Whence hath this great tribute come unto thee save that thou madest men afeard of thee till they yielded thee this scot?"

Then said the giant Urgan: "Tristram, thou profferest me great bobaunce that thou hinderest me to drive my cattle. Withdraw thee with all the haste thou mayest from the path of my cattle that I have used to go. I am not Morhaut that thou slewest with thy violence, and I am not the men of Ireland that thou stolest Ysolt from, yet thou thinkest to have ado with me. But wit thou well that thou shalt buy it dear that thou lettest me the passage of the bridge."

And with that he brandished his iron club, and flang it with all his might and great wrath: but Tristram avoided the stroke: but the iron club smote the horse's breast and brake it all in sunder and brast his leg and the horse fell under him. When Tristram stood on foot, he rushed upon him as fast as he might to strike him when he might best come nigh him and reach him with his hands. When the giant bent down to take the iron club Tristram would no longer tarry and dashed at him and struck from him the right hand, wherewith he would take up the club, and the hand lay there in the grass. Now when the giant saw his hand lie on the field, he seized his club with his left hand and would quit him upon Tristram and he struck at him. Then

Tristram set his shield against that buffet and the shield was cloven in sunder endlong in two pieces: and the stroke was so heavy that Tristram fell on his knee and he perceived that if he abode another stroke he would be slain: so he gave aback. And when he saw the giant was sore wounded and dismayed and bleeding much, he cast him to hold until the bleeding should weaken him and minish his strength. Howbeit the giant took up his hand and left his cattle standing and yode home to his castle, but Tristram abode whole and unharmed, with full mickle joy that now all the cattle were delivered and won again. He wist now in certain that he would get that he asked but if the Duke brake covenant with him; but him thought now that it was not possible to return, for he had nothing he might show unto the Duke for to ensure him that he hath encountered with the giant but if he should drive back the cattle.

So he hied him as he best might along the track thereas the giant's wound bled and came anon unto the giant's castle. When he entered therein, he saw naught there save the hand and hastened therewith as fast as he might again unto the bridge. In the meanwhile the giant returned him unto the castle, for he had gone to bind himself with herb salve, and he thought he should find there his hand. When he had laid down the herbs, he perceived that his hand was borne away, and he hastened after Tristram. Then Tristram looked behind him and espied his coming, and he came leaping after him with great noise and he had on his shoulder his iron club: and then Tristram was afeard for the giant that he durst not go against him. Then the giant began to assault him and cast the iron club at him with great wrath and all his strength, and he sprang aside so that the blow struck him not. Then Tristram dashed upon him, and would smite him on the left side, and when he saw the giant escape that stroke, he gave him a buffet afore and it was so heavy that he shore away all his shoulder and hurled him down backward from the bridge and all the bones in him brast. Then Tristram went and took his hands and went to the Duke. But he had been in the forest and beheld their combat, and when he saw Tristram, he rode against him and speered how it had fared. Tristram showed him the thing he had even now performed, freed the cattle and slain the giant: then said he unto the Duke:

"Now I crave my gift."

Then answered him the Duke: "That is right. I will not deny it you. Say now what it best liketh you to have."

"Gramercy," said Tristram. "I slew Urgan, and now I desire that ye give me your fair dog, for right fain would I possess him, sithen I saw never fairer 'dog."

Then said the Duke: "By my faith, ye slew our most foe, and for that I will grant you the half of my realm and give you my sister with honor if ye would ask her. But if my dog delight you more, then gladly ye shall have him."

Then said Tristram: "God reward you, my lord. There is no treasure in this world that is to me so dear as the dog, and therefore never will I yield him up for all that may be proffered."

Then said the Duke: "Come now hither and take him and do with him as ye will."

Chapter lxiii

WHEN he had taken the dog, he would not let him go though all the riches that be in the world were proffered him. And he called unto him a minstrel, the most courteous man that he might find in all that duchy, and said unto him privily what he should do and whither he should go and in what wise he should bear the dog unto Tintagel to Queen Ysolt. And the minstrel went thither and found Bringvain, the Queen's gentlewoman, and betaught the dog unto her and bade her give him unto the Queen from Tristram, and the Queen received him with much joy and many thanks, for never might be fairer creature. For him was there made with great cunning a house of pure gold, and locked well, and to Ysolt was this present most precious above all things. And Ysolt gave in reward rich gifts unto Tristram's messenger, and sent him word that the King was now well disposed to himward, and that he should come back in safety, for that all the suspicions men had unto him were turned now unto reconcilement and accord. When Tristram heard

these tidings, he went again with mickle joy to King
Mark's court. In such wise was this dog won and
enchieved. I will now do you to wit that Tristram's
dog was not long in Mark's court. He was wont
to go out into the wood to hunt wild swine and red
deer as at that time when Tristram and Ysolt dwelt
there both together. This dog caught every beast
t'hat he never failed, and was so sure of scent that
he tracked all manner paths and slots.

Chapter lxiv

NOW when Tristram was comen unto King
Mark's court with great glee and mirth, he
was not there long ere the King discovered again
the great love of Tristram and the Queen, either
to other, even as before. And he was araged and
made great dole of this and would not endure it
more and put them both in outlawry, but this seemed
them rather a goodly fortune. And they went forth
into the great wilderness and thought little thereof
who should purvey them wine and victual, for God
would give them some nouriture wheresoever they
were. And right well it pleased these twain to dwell
alone together, and they craved naught more than
they had then of all that they possessed in the
world, for now have they that which delighteth their
minds, if only they may ever be together without
blame and use their love with play.

And because it liked them this freedom in the

forest, they found a secret place beside a certain water and in a rock that heathen men let hew and adorn in olden time with mickle skill and fair craft, and this was all vaulted and the entrance digged deep into the earth, and there was a secret path far beneath. Over the house lay much earth and thereon stood a right fair tree upon a rock, and the shade of the tree spreading abroad gave defense from the sun's heat and burning. By the house was a fountain with clean water; round the water grew the sweetest herbs with fair blossoms that men might choose, and a stream ran from the fountain toward the east. When the sun shone upon the grass it smelled with the sweetest smell, and the water was all as it had been mixed with honey for the sweetness of the herbs. What time it rained and the cold was great, then were they in their house under the rock, but when it was good weather without, they yode unto the fountain to play and about in the wood there it was most level and fairest to walk and to hunt beasts to feed them withal: for Tristram had there with him his hound that was dearest to him. There first he trained the dog to take red deer, and he chased them as many as Tristram would. Great pleasaunce and joy was it unto them, for they had night and day their lust and solace.

Chapter lxv

THEN on a day it befell by adventure that the King, as he was wont, came into the wood with a great company of hunters, and they loosed their slot-hounds and laid ambushes and blew their horns and urged their hounds and dashed hither and thither into the wood till that they found a great herd of dear. Then they severed from them all the biggest and the deer began to run divers ways, some up the mountains, some down the dales thereas they wist the hardest places were to follow, and thus the deer won upon the hounds. The hunters rode their horses after and blew their horns. The King departed from his meynie and followed two of his best hounds, and with him went certain hunters that had the charge of his hounds. And they chased a great hart and set him in flight and drove him strongly, and he fled all that he might by divers ways, and he shaped his course toward a river. And when he came unto the banks, he stood still and listened about him, and he heard behind him the approach of the hounds, though yet far away, and he knew then that the hunters came straight behind him. Then he turned him again another way that the hounds might not be ware of him and leapt with a great leap across the river, and straightway thence into the river and again out of the water. And so the hounds lost him and wist not where he was become, and the King lamented much of this misadventure. Now the master hunter hight Kanves, and he rode now up, now down, to put the hounds upon the scent: but the hounds sought wide and found not the track, and Kanves came to a stand and looked up at a rock: there beside he saw the path nigh the spring, for Tristram and Ysolt had gone there in the morning early to disport them. When Kanves saw the path, him thought that the hart might there have taken his way or have stopped there to rest him, and forthwith he alight from his horse for to discover what was betid, and he went along the path that led unto the rock till he came unto a door therein. He looked in and saw Tristram sleeping and on the other side of the house Ysolt. They had lain down for to rest them for the great heat, and for this cause they slept so far either from other that they had afore gone forth to play. When he beheld them, he was so adread that he quaked by reason of a great sword lay betwixt them, and he fled unto the King and said unto him:

"Lord, I have not found the deer," and he told the King all the adventure that he had seen in the house of the rock, and said he wist not whether it were thing heavenly or earthly or of faerye.

Chapter lxvi

NOW went the King thither and saw Tristram and knew Ysolt and the sword that he had himself possessed: no sword was there in the world sharper of edge than that which lay betwixt these two lovers. Then the King saw that each of them was far from the other, and him seemed, then, that if sinful lust were betwixt them, certes would they not lie so far each from other, rather would they have one bed. And she seemed him wonderly fair, and he looked upon her face, and she seemed him then so fair that he thought never had he seen fairer, for in weariness she slept and there was redness in her cheeks. But through a hole that was in the house, a sunbeam shone in on her cheek, and it annoyed him much that the sun shone upon her face, and he yode then as quietly as he might unto her and laid his glove upon her cheek to defend her from the sun. Then went he forth and commended them unto God and went away from the rock sorrowful. Then the hunter bade the squires they should drive together the dogs, for the King would go home from hunting, and he rode alone, woeful and heavy, and no man followed him unto his tent. When Ysolt awoke, she found the glove and it seemed her strange by what chance the King's glove was comen there, and in like wise seemed this marvelous unto Tristram, and they wist not what they should do, inasmuch as the King knew where they

[181]

were. But yet was it much joy and solace unto them that he found them in such wise as then he saw them and for that cause might find no wrong in them.

And now King Mark will by no mean believe evil nor slander against Tristram and Ysolt, and he assummoned all his barons and showed them that by right and reason that was falseness and felony that was shown and noised concerning Tristram, and it behoved no man follow nor believe it nor hold it for certain. When they heard his reason and proof, them thought as he would have Ysolt home again, and they counseled him as seemed best and most pleasing unto them and according as his own desire most leaned. Then he sent for them that they should come home in peace and joy for that he had removed his wrath from them.

Chapter lxvii

BUT Tristram might by no mean restrain his will and desire, and therefore he used every occasion that he might attain unto it, and he fared thus until on a day they lay both together in a garden and Tristram held [1] Queen Ysolt in his embrace, and well they thought them safe. By strange adventure there cometh upon them the King, the which the dwarf leadeth thither. He thought to take them with the deed, but thanked be God, when he found

[1] *Here endeth Brother Robert and beginneth Master Thomas.*

them sleeping, they were in seemly case. The King beheld them and said unto the dwarf:

"Abide me here a little space. I will go up into the palace and bring hither some of my barons: they shall behold how we have found them. Brent shall they be when it shall be proved upon them."

Therewithal Tristram awoke and espied the King, but made no semblaunt till he was departed unto the palace. Tristram arose and said: "Alas, Ysolt, my love, awake thee now. With treason are we waited. The King hath espied all we have done, and goeth unto the palace for his men. He will, if he may, cause us to be taken together and by his sentence brent to ashes. I will go away, fair love: dread thee not for thy life, for thou canst not be proved guilty if no man be found here save thee alone. But I will repair me forth into another land, and for thy sake will I flee mirths and seek exile, despise joy and follow jeopardy. Such dole have I for this parting, never more shall I have delight the days of my life. My sweet lady, I pray thee, never put me out of thy remembrance: love me when I am from thee far as thou hast loved me near. I dare not, lady, longer abide. Now as I take my leave, kiss me."

From that kiss Ysolt held back and hearkened his words and saw his tears: her eyes streamed and from her heart she sighed and tenderly said: "My love, fair sir, well it behoveth thee to have in remembrance this day when thou departest in such dolorous case. Such pain have I of this parting that never before have I known sorrow. No more, love, shall I have disport when I have lost thy solace, no more shall I have such pity nor such yearning sithen it befalleth me to part from thy love. Our bodies now must sunder, but love from us shall not sunder. In the mean while take thou this ring: for my love's sake, my lover, guard it:[2] it shall be for writing and seal, surety and solace to mind us of our loves and of this parting."

They parted then with much mourning and kissed together right heartily.

Chapter lxviii

NOW Tristram went his way, but Ysolt was left behind weeping and tossed with many torments. In like wise weeping sore, Tristram went forth and leaped over the garden wall. Then came the King unto Ysolt and made accusation against her, and with him came his barons, and found there no man save her alone, and therefore might they give her no blame, for naught evil did she do, and the King forwent his wrath against her. But Tristram went full of care to his hostel and made him ready hastily and all his fellows. So they rode unto the strand and went on a ship and sailed from that realm and landed up in Normandy: but they dwelt there not long. And Tristram wandered from one

[2] *Here endeth Master Thomas and beginneth Brother Robert again.*

land to another to seek adventures that he might accomplish: he endured many trials and weariness ere he enchieved honor and worship, rest and comfort. Then he served the princes and kaysers of Rome and was long in the realm. Then he journeyed into Spain and thence into Brittany to the heritage of Roald his fosterfather, and they received him with great joy, worshiped him and honored him, and gave unto him a great domain and many castles free under his power, loving him with true love, and helped him in every need, and did him to know unknown men, and followed him to tourneys, and they spread the fame of his prowess and valor.

Chapter lxix

IN those days reigned over that realm an old duke, and his neighbors wrought him much noyance and strong battles: all they were full mighty and great and they pressed him sore for that they had great lust unto the castle thereas he dwelt. This duke had three sons, valiant men: the eldest hight Kaherdin; he was a fair man and a courteous and right good fellow unto Tristram. And they gave Tristram a rich castle because of his puissance that he should drive away their enemies. And he did so much that he took of them many men and wasted their fortresses and waged war against them so long with Kaherdin's help that naught else remained for them to do but to beg mercy for themselves and make peace.

Kaherdin had a fair, gentle, and courteous sister, and wise above all women that were in that land, and she hight Ysolt, and Tristram had a fantasy unto her and gave her love-gifts, and for the sake of that Ysolt for whom he grieved he spake with her of love and she with him, and he made then many love-songs with sweet minstrelsy and fitting words and all manner of lays, and often in his songs he sang:

"Ysolt ma drue, Ysolt m'amie,
En vous ma mort, en vous ma vie!"

Tristram sang his songs afore knights and lords in halls and chambers, in hearing of many people, Ysolt and her kin, and all thought it was said of her and that he loved none other than this Ysolt. And all her kin were well pleased, and of all Kaherdin most and his brethren, for he thought that Tristram loved Ysolt, their sister and would wish to dwell there for their love's sake, for they had approved him a knight so good that they wished to love and serve him. They set all their care to bring their sister unto him in friendship, and they led him unto the damozel's chamber to solace him there with her and to hold converse with her, for through mirth and speech riseth tenderness and often are the hearts of men turned. Thus was Tristram now greatly abashed as touching his governance:[1] his

[1] *Here Master Thomas beginneth again.*

[186]

heart often changed and much he studied in divers
ways how he might change his will sith he might
not have his desire, and he said:

"Ysolt, fair friend, how different been our lives.
Your love hath so departed from me that it serveth
not save to deceive me. For you I lose joy and liking, but ye have them both night and day. I lead
my life in great dole, but ye yours in delights of
love. I do naught save desire you, but ye may not
escape from delight and joy and from doing all
your pleasures. For your body I live in pain: but
the King hath his joy of you; his delight he hath
thereof and pleasure: that which was mine is now
his. Howbeit I quitclaim of that I may not have,
for well I wot she disporteth her therein: me she
hath forgotten for her pleasaunce. But in my heart
I hold all other in despite for Ysolt alone. Nowise
doth she recomfort me, yet she knoweth well my
great dolor and anguish that I endure for her love.
For of another am I much desired and for this
cause grievously am I tormented: if such demand
were not of my love, I might better suffer my own
longing: but by reason of this pursuit I doubt I shall
leave my old love, if she take not heed. Sith I
may not have my love, it behoveth me take that I
may, for meseemeth I must needs do so: this doth
he that can do no more. What availeth it to wait
so long and to eschew good all his days? What
availeth it to maintain love of which no good may
betide? Such pains, such woes have I suffered for
her love that I may not win good of them. It

profiteth naught to keep it. Of her am I all forgot, for that her heart is changed.

"Ah fair father God, King of heaven, how might that change be? How might she change when in me love abideth still? How might she forsake love? Never for no cause may I depart from it. I wot well an my heart were departed therefrom, she had felt it by her own. Nor evil nor good nor naught might she do that my heart had not felt it straightway: and by my own heart have I well felt that hers hath kept faith toward me and comforted me unto her power. If I may not have my desire, I ought not for that run to change, and leave her for a stranger. For we be so possessed and our hearts so aggrieved with love that an I may not win my desire, behoveth me restrain myself unto my power. So far as she may, she hath the will if she had but the power; and she ought not suffer my ill will if, when she doth the will of the King, she doth not my desire: I know not what loathing she may have of it. Ysolt, how little soever your power may be, ye have right good will unto me.

"How then might she change? Nor may I then be false to my love. Well I wot if she list to change, my heart would feel it in short space. In sooth, whatsomever there be of change, I feel full well this sundering: yea, in my heart right well I feel that she loveth me little or naught: for if in her heart she loved me most, by some mean she would give me comfort. Of what? Of this sorrow. Where should she find me? Where I am. Perchance she knoweth not where nor in what land. Well, she might forsooth seek me. To what end? Because of my sorrow. She dareth not for her lord, although she might desire it. Of what avail when she may not have it? She loveth her lord, holdeth to him, and asketh not to remember me. Well, I blame her not if she forget me, for never behoveth her languish for me: her great beauty doth not require it nor doth it befit her nature that when she hath all her desire of Mark she ought to languish for another. So ought she to delight her in the King that she should forget her love of me: to delight her in her lord that she should forget her lover. What availeth now my love in comparison with the love of her husband? Naturally should she so do, sith that she may not fare according unto her desire. Let her hold to that she may have, for she must leave that she loveth. Let her take that she may have and ordain it unto her will. Through often kissing and playing she may accord this matter with him. Soon will she be able such disport to have that she will remember me naught. And if she remember not, what boots it me? Let her do well or not, I take no force. Without love, joy may she have and delight as well I wot.

"Yet how may it be that without love she should have pleasaunce or love her lord, or how put in forgetfulness what she hath had so much in remembrance? How cometh joy to a man of hating that he hath one time loved or of bearing wrath and hate toward that therein he had one time set his heart? What he hath loved he ought not hate, but he may well depart and remove him when he seeth therein no cause to love. He ought not hate nor love beyond that he seeth cause therein. When he beholdeth deed of noblesse and upon that another of villainy, him behoveth so to attend to the noblesse that he may not render back evil for evil. The one deed ought so to atone for the other that betwixt them they should prevent, by reason of the villainy from overmuch loving, and by reason of the noblesse from overmuch hating. The noblesse one ought therefore to love and the villainy to fear, nor ought one to hate because of the noblesse, nor ought one to serve because of the villainy. For that Ysolt hath loved me and made me such great countenance of joy, I ought not to hate her for aught that may betide, and when she forgetteth our love, I ought not to remember her more. I ought not to have loved her ere this, nor ought I now to hate her so much.

"But now would I if I may withdraw from her as she doth from me, and by works and deeds to essay how I may find delight in deeds that are against love as she doth with her lord. How may I prove this but if I espouse a wife? Indeed she had had no cause for doing as she doth had she not been lawfully wedded, for it is her lawful marriage that causeth the departing of our love. Forsooth, ought she not to forsake him, and whatsomever desire he hath behoveth her do. But nowise am I now constrained to do but if I would essay her manner of life. Yea, to know the Queen's estate, will I espouse this damozel, to wit whether wedlock and union may make me forget, like as she for her lord hath forgotten our love. I do it not for hate, but for this cause will I forsake her and love her as she loveth me, that I may wit how she loveth the King."

Tristram is in right great anguish of this love that he might accomplish, and in great debate and trial. Other reason he findeth none but that he would prove at last if in despite of love he might take delight and if by the delight he desired he might forget Ysolt, for he weened that she forgat him for her lord and her delight. For this cause he would espouse a wife that Ysolt might not blame him that against reason he sought such delight as beseemed not his prowess. Ysolt as Blanches Mains he desired for her beauty and for her name Ysolt: for the beauty alone that was in her, he had not desired her if she had not the name Ysolt, nor for the name without the beauty. These two things that are in her cause him undertake this enterprise, to wit that he would espouse the damozel for to know the estate of the Queen, and how he might have pleasaunce with his wife in despite of love. He on his half would essay how Ysolt wrought with the King, and he would for this cause essay what pleasaunce he would have with Ysolt as Blanches Mains. For his dolor and his grief Tristram would fain have vengeance: yet for his malady he seeketh such vengeance as will double his torment: he would deliver him from pain, but he doth naught save encumber him: he thought to have pleasaunce when he might not have his desire. Tristram noted in the damozel the name and the beauty of the Queen: for her name alone he had not taken her nor for her beauty had she not been Ysolt: had she not been called Ysolt, Tristram had not loved her. By reason of the name and the beauty that he found in her, he fell in desire and longing to have the damozel.

Hearken now a marvelous adventure, how that men are of strange nature and in no wise stable. Of nature are they so variant that though they may not leave of their evil custom, yet they may change their good custom. Unto evil are they so used that evil custom they hold all their days and so work villainy that they know not what noblesse is, and so do treason that they forget courtesy: in malice they strive so exceedingly that all their life they abide therein; from evil they may not depart, so are they wont to use it. Some are hardened in evil, other some tend unto good. All the purpose of their life is in change and newfangleness, and their good power they forsake for to take their evil desire. Newfangleness causeth to forsake their good power for their evil desire and to leave the good that they may have but for to delight in ill. Man leaveth the best that he hath for to take a less good thing that longeth unto another: that which is his he holdeth for worse, while that of others he coveteth for better. An the good that he hath were not his, he had not despised it in his heart: but that which it behoveth him to have, he may not heartily love. If he might not have that he hath, he had not longed to win it: he would think to find it better than his own: and for this cause he may not love his own. It is newfangleness deceiveth him when he desireth not that which he ought to have, and that which he hath not desireth, and leaveth his own to take a worse thing. Behoveth him that may to change the evil, to leave the worse and take the better, to do wisdom and eschew folly: for he is not fickle that changeth to amend himself for to remove himself from evil usage. But oft a fickle man runneth in his heart after change and thinketh to find in new thing that which he may not in his own: it is that which changeth his intent: that he hath not he would fain essay, and afterward he repenteth him. Ladies in like wise are wont thus to do: they leave that they have for that they desire and essay how they may attain unto their will and their desire. I wot not, certes, what I say thereof: but overmuch they love newfangle thing, both men and ladies, for overmuch they change their longing and will and desire against reason and beyond their power. One would advance him in love, yet doth naught but impair him: one thinketh to cast away love, yet increaseth his sorrow twofold; one purposeth vengeance, yet falleth in grievous woe; and one thinketh to deliver him, yet doth naught save to encumber him.

Tristram thought to forsake Ysolt and to tear love from his heart, and by espousing the other Ysolt would he deliver him from the first Ysolt: and if the first Ysolt had not been, he had not so loved the other: because it is Ysolt he hath loved, now he intendeth well to love Ysolt, but because that he may not have the first, he hath desire unto the second: if he might have Ysolt, the Queen, he had not loved Ysolt, the maid. Therefore, meseemeth it ought to be said that this was neither love nor wrath, for an this were true love, he had not loved the maid despite his desire for his lady: yet was this not true hatred, for only through love of the Queen did Tristram love the maiden. Since he wedded by reason of his love, it was not then for hatred, for if he hated Ysolt of his heart, he had not for love of her taken the other Ysolt, but if he had loved her with true love, he had not espoused the other Ysolt. But so it befell as at this time that he was so tormented of love that he would fain work against love to deliver him from love. Natheless to deliver him from dolor, he fell into a greater. This befalleth many men: when they have sore travail and anguish and great pain and distress, such things they do to escape and deliver and avenge them as thereof cometh great harm: often they do of purpose thing whereof they endure sorrow. I have seen it betide unto many that, when they may not have their desire or thing that they love, they strive unto their utmost power: of their distress they do such deeds whereby ofttimes they double their grief, and when they would deliver them, may not escape. In this deed of vengeance, I perceive both love and wrath, nor is it love alone nor hate alone, but wrath is mixed with love, and love is mixed with wrath. Whosoever doth that he desireth not to do because that he may not have some good thing, doth his will despite his desire; and Tristram doth even so: despite his desire he achieveth his will. Because that he hath woe of Ysolt, through Ysolt will he deliver him. And much he kisseth and clippeth her, and much he speaketh with her parents: all are accorded concerning the marriage, he to take and she to give herself.

Chapter lxx

THE day is named, the term appointed: and Tristram cometh thither with his friends, and the Duke is there also with his. All the purveyance is ready: Tristram espouseth Ysolt as Blanches Mains. The chaplain saith mass and whatsoever longeth unto the service, after the ordinance of Holy Church. Then they go to eat the feast, and thereafter to disport them at quintain and jousts, javelins and reeds, wrestling and fencing, in many games of strife, such as long unto feasts and as folk of the world require. The day passed with mirth. The bed is ready against the night. They make the maiden to lay her therein, and Tristram doth off the gown wherewith he was clad: well it sitteth

upon him, close at the wrists. As they remove
the robe, they take off the ring of his finger, the
which Ysolt gave him in the garden that last day
that he spake with her. Tristram looketh and seeth
the ring, and a new thought entereth: with that
thought is he in great anguish that he wot not what
he may do. Now is his power contrary to that
which his will may do, and he museth then so
straightly that he repenteth him of his deed. Loth
is it unto him and in his heart he draweth him therefrom: by the ring that he seeth on his finger he is
sore abashed. He remembereth him of the covenant that he made at that parting and that sundering
in the garden. From the depth of his heart he uttereth a sigh and saith to himself:

"How may I fare? This deed is to me loth.
Natheless behoveth me couch with her as with my
lawful wife: behoveth me lie with her for I may
not forsake her. This cometh all of my foolish
heart, that was so gay and light when I demanded
the maid of her parents and her friends. Little I
thought then of Ysolt, my lady, when I wrought
this folly to betray and break my faith. Though
it grieveth me, I must lie with her. I have espoused
her lawfully at the door of the church and in the
sight of men. I may never refuse her, and it behoveth me do folly. Without great sin and wrong
I may not withdraw me, yet may I not meddle with
her but if I break my faith; for so much have I
wrought with the other Ysolt that not with reason
may this Ysolt have me. Unto this Ysolt I owe

so much that I may not keep faith with the other, and yet my faith I ought not break, nor ought I forsake this maiden. I break my faith to Ysolt, my lady, if in my life I have pleasaunce of another, and if of this maiden I have disport, then shall I do sin and trespass and wrong. For I may not leave her; yet I ought not have pleasaunce of lying with her in bed for mine ease and my delight, for so much have I dealt with the Queen, beseemeth me not to lie with the maid; yet with the maid have I so wrought that there is for me no withdrawal. I ought neither betray Ysolt nor leave my wife: I ought not part from her, nor ought I lie with her. If with this maid I hold my covenant, then I break my affiance with Ysolt, and if I hold faith with Ysolt, then am I unto my wife disloyal. To her beseemeth me not be disloyal, nor would I work in the despite of Ysolt. I know not which of them to deceive, for one must I betray and deceive and beguile or else I trow I shall betray both. Already have I approached this maiden so nigh that I have been false to Ysolt: howbeit I have so loved the Queen that the maiden is beguiled, and so sore am I beguiled that to the damage of both one and the other have I known them. Both one and the other are grieved for me, and I am grieved for the two Ysolts. Both are smitten for my love, and with them both I break faith. With the Queen have I already broken faith, yet may I not keep it with her for whose sake it behoved me to be faithless. To one at least I may keep troth: sithen I have broken it with the Queen, I ought to keep it with the maid, for I may not leave her: but yet I ought not betray the other Ysolt.

"Certes, I wot not what I should do. Of all halves I have great anguish, for evil is it to keep my troth, but worse to forsake my wife. Howsomever it may betide as touching my pleasure, behoveth me now to lie in her bed. Of Ysolt do I thus avenge me, sith I was first of her beguiled: of Ysolt I would avenge me, for of her beguiled was I first. In her despite have I brought so much upon me that I know not what to do. If I lie with my wife, Ysolt will be right wroth thereof. But if I will not sleep with her, it will turn to my reproach and of her should I have evil anger, and of her kin and all other should I be hated and despised, and towards God should I sin. I fear me of the shame, and I fear me of the sin. If when I shall lie beside her, I do not that which in my heart I most hate and is most against my will, no pleasaunce shall I have of my lying. She will understand that unto my power I have greater love towards another: simple will she be an she discover not that I love and covet another more, and liefer would I lie where I may delight me more. If she hath not her pleasure of me, I trow she will love me little, and of right will she hate me therefor if I withhold me from the natural deed that should bind us in love. Of abstinence will come hate: for as love cometh of the doing, so cometh hate of the refraining. An I refrain me from the deed, I shall endure dolor and grief, and my prowess and bounty shall be turned unto villainy: that I have conquered by my valor, shall I now lose by this love. Whatsomever love she hath toward me will now be withdrawn by reason of my refraining. All my service and my nobleness will be lost for my recreance. Without the deed much hath she loved me and coveted in her thought: now will she hate me for refraining insomuch as she hath not her desire: for this it is that most bindeth in love lover and beloved.

"Yet for this very cause will I not do it, for I would dissuade her from loving: well would I that hatred were hers; rather than love I now desire it. Overmuch have I drawn her unto me. As touching my lady have I done ill, that above all other hath loved me, and of which cometh unto me this desire, this longing, this will, this force, this power that caused me approach this maid and wed her despite of love and despite of the faith I owe to Ysolt my love. Yet will I more betray her when more near I would approach her. By my words I seek occasion, guile, countenance, and reason to break my faith with Ysolt, for that I would lie with this maiden, and despite my love I seek occasion to have disport of her. But beseemeth me not to prove faithless so long as Ysolt, my lady, liveth. What treason and felony I do when I win somewhat in despite of love. Already have I won much whereof I shall have sorrow the term of my life. For the wrong that I have done, I will that my lady have right, and penance shall I endure thereof after my deserving. I will now lie in this bed, and yet shall abstain me from delight. Wit ye well no torment may I have whereof I shall endure often greater pain nor whereof I shall have greater anguish, whether there be betwixt us wrath or love. For if I should desire pleasaunce of her, then will it be hard to endure her bed. Either love or hatred will be hard and grievous to suffer: but because I have broken my faith unto Ysolt, I take such like punishment upon me. When she will know how I am tormented, she ought so much to pardon me."

Tristram lieth down, Ysolt halseth him, and kisseth his mouth and face, and straineth him unto her, sigheth from her heart and desireth that which he desireth not: for it is against his will either to forbear his pleasure or to do it: his nature would fain discover itself, but his reason holdeth him unto Ysolt. The love he hath unto the Queen removeth his desire unto the maiden. Love removeth desire so that Nature hath no power: Love and Reason constrain him and overcome the lust of his body. The great love he hath unto Ysolt removeth that which Nature willeth and overcometh this lust that without love filleth his mind. He hath strong liking unto the deed, but love strongly compelleth him to refrain. He feeleth the maiden sweet, fair he knoweth her, and he longeth for his pleasaunce, and hateth his love, for had he not so great love, he might assent him unto his desire. But unto his great love he yieldeth him, and in great pain is he and torment, in mickle study and anguish, for he knoweth not how he may abstain nor what countenance he should make towards his wife and by what device he ought to cover him. Natheless he is a little abashed and fleeth that which he desireth, escheweth his pleasure, and fleeth so that he took not his delight. Then said Tristram:

"My fair lady, take it not for villainy: I would confess to thee a secret so that I pray thee much to cover it that none may know thereof but only we: never told I this ere I tell it now unto thee. Here in my right side I have an infirmity that hath held me right long. This night it hath tormented me sore, and through the great travail that I have dured is it awakened throughout my body. Such anguish holdeth me and so nigh doth it approach unto my liver that I dare not have joy nor weary me by reason of this evil. Never have I wearied me but a little but I swooned thrice and sick have I been long after. Be not heavy if now we leave our play: we shall yet enjoy it when I shall desire and thou also."

"Heavy am I for thy malady," answered Ysolt, "more than for any other malady in the world, but of that whereof I hear thee speak I will well that we refrain us."

Chapter lxxi

QUEEN YSOLT sigheth in her chamber for Tristram, that she so desireth, nor may she muse in her heart of aught save only the love of

Tristram. She hath none other longing nor other love nor other hope. In him is all her desire, yet may she hear naught of him: she knoweth not where he is become, nor in what land, nor if he be dead or living. For this cause is she in great sorrow, nor for a long time hath she heard aught sooth. She knoweth not that he is in Brittany, but thinketh him in Spain, thereas he slew the giant, nephew unto the great Orguilus, the which came from Africa to defy princes and kings from land to land. Orguilus was hardy and valiant and he fought with all men: many he discomfited and slew and took the beards from their chins, and a mantle he made of great beards, wide and well flowing. He heard tell of King Arthur, the which had passing great honor in the land, for such was his prowess and worthiness that he was never vanquished in battle, and with many had he fought and vanquished them all. When the giant heard this, he sent unto him as it had been his friend that he had a new mantle, though it lacked a border and tassels, the which was wrought of the beards of kings and barons and princes of other regions the which he had over-comen in battle or slain with strength in stour, and thereof he had made such a garment as befitteth the beards of kings, but the border was yet lacking. And because that Arthur is the most high and wor-shipful king of the land, he sent unto him that for his love he should cut off his beard and send it unto him for his boast, for he will do him such honor that he will place it above all the others. Even as he is a high king and sovereign over the others, so will his beard be exalted if he will cut it off for him. Right high will he set it on the mantle and make thereof border and tassels, but if he will not send it, he will do with him as he is wont to do. He will stake his mantle against his beard, and will have ado with him, and he that may win the battle shall have both mantle and beard without fail. When Arthur heard this speech, he had woe and anger in his heart, and he returned answer unto the giant that he would fight ere he would yield up his beard for dread as a recreant. When the giant heard that the King so answered him, he came right fiercely as far as the marches of his land to demand the beard, and to fight with him. They met then together and staked the mantle and the beard, and then with great wrath did they fight: mighty battle and sharp strife they made all the day. But the morn Arthur vanquished him, and took away his mantle and his head. Through prowess and valor he won this adventure, and freed from the giant the lands of kings and earls, and punished him for his bobaunce and malice.

Unto the matter this pertaineth not, but it is good that I tell you that this giant whereof now I speak was nephew unto him that would have the beards; and he came to demand the beard of the King and Emperor, whom as at this time Tristram served, when yet he was in Spain and ere he repaired him to Brittany. The King would not give it unto him, but he found not in his land among his kinsmen and his friends one who would defend his beard or encounter the giant, and thereof was he sore distressed and made dole in the hearing of all his people. Then Tristram emprised it for his love and gave the giant a right hard battle and full stiff encounter. For both was it dolorous: there was Tristram sore smitten and wounded and grieved of his body, and woe were his friends therefor, but the giant was slain. Of this wound by fortune never had Queen Ysolt heard, for it is the wont of envy to say much of evil and naught of the good, for envy hideth good deeds and spreadeth evil works. The wise man therefore saith in ancient scripture:

"Better it profiteth to be without company than to have company of envy, and better night and day without fellow than to have one where no love is." Envy will hide the good that he knoweth, and, because he hateth, he will tell the evil. If one doth well, he will say naught thereof, but he will hide the ill from no man. Therefore is it better to lack a fellow than to company with such as naught cometh from save evil. Tristram had companions enow of whom he was hated or little loved, and such there were about King Mark that loved him not nor held faith. The good they heard they kept from Ysolt, but the evil they spread wide: they would not tell the good they heard unto the Queen, that desired it, but because they envied her, they told her that which she most hated.

Chapter lxxii

ON a day she sat in her chamber and made a piteous lay of love, how that Lord Gurun was surprised and slain for love of a lady the which he loved above all thing, and how by guile the Count gave the heart of Gurun unto his wife one day to eat, and the dole which the lady made when she wist that her lover was dead. The lady Ysolt sang sweetly and her voice accorded with the instrument: fair were her hands, the lay good, sweet her voice, and low her tone. Then came Cariadoc, a rich earl of great heritage, of fair castles and rich land: and to require the Queen of love hath he come unto the court. But Ysolt holdeth it great folly, for oft had he sought it already ere Tristram left the court. Now came he to woo her, but never might he speed nor might he win of the Queen so much as the value of a glove: neither in promise nor in gift gat he naught ever. Natheless, much hath he dwelt in the court and sojourned for his love. He was a right fair knight and thereto courteous and proud and haughty, but little was he to praise as touching his bearing arms. He was full likely and ready of speech, a fair gallant and a good jester. He found Ysolt singing a lay and said laughing:

"Lady, well I know that when one heareth the owl cry, men are wont to speak of death, for his cry signifieth death: and your song, I trow, signi-

fieth the death of the owl himself. Some owl hath
now lost his life."

" 'Tis sooth ye say," Ysolt said unto him. "I will
well that it signifieth his death. Certes he is a
screech-owl or other manner owl of whose song
men are dismayed. Well ought ye to fear your own
death sith my singing dismayeth you, for ye be an owl
certes for the tidings ye bring. Never, I trow,
brought ye tidings whereof I was glad, nor never
came ye hither that ye told me not evil tidings. It
shall be with you as it was with a slothful man, that
never arose from the doorway save it were to chide
a man. From your hostel ye issue never but if ye
have heard a tale that ye may tell after, but ye go
not far abroad to do a deed that other men may
tell. Concerning you one heareth never a tale
whereof your friends may take honor nor those that
hate you, sorrow. Ye would fain tell the deeds of
other men: your own will never be had in remembrance."

Cariadoc then answered: "Ye be angry, but
wherefore I wot not. A fool is he who is dismayed
of your words. If I be a screech-owl, then are ye
an owl in like wise. Whatsoever may betide of my
death, I bring you evil tidings concerning Tristram,
your lover. Ye have lost him, my lady Ysolt: in
another land hath he taken him a wife. Henceforth
ye may seek after him, for he disdaineth your love
and hath taken a wife of much worship, the Duke's
daughter of Brittany."

Ysolt answered in great scorn: "Always have ye

been a screech-owl to speak evil of Sir Tristram. God grant I may never have good if I be not an owl as touching you. Ye have told me evil tidings, to you will I never tell good. Sooth is it ye say that in vain ye love me: never shall ye have favor of me: nor you nor your lusts shall I love never the term of my life. A foul thing had I gained, had I received your love; liefer would I lose his than win yours. Wit ye well of these tidings ye have mentioned unto me shall ye never have profit."

She is wood wroth and Cariadoc perceiveth it well: he would not with further speech give her pain nor reproach her nor enrage her, and from her chamber he hieth speedily. Ysolt now maketh great dole, and in her heart she is anguished and wroth of these tidings,[1] and complaineth her with these words:

"Now may no one put trust in man. Never more it behoveth to trust in another's love. Now is he also become a traitor, for he hath taken him a wife in another land."

So made she her moan of their departition.

Chapter lxxiii

TRISTRAM abode now in his woe, but yet he made semblaunt as he were blithe and merry, and never he let it be noted of him that he was somedele in pain and misery: and in this wise he hid

---

[1] *Here Brother Robert taketh up the tale.*

his misery that he went to disport him on hunting
with the Duke himself and all his noblest friends.
There also was Kaherdin, the Duke's son, and two
other sons of his, right fair men, and there also
were his noblest lords. And they sought to follow
the hounds and hunters, and rode another way
under a wood to a water, and looked about to see
what had happened on the march of his lands, for
that water was a bound mark, and there had they
oft endured stern fights and hard encounters. On
this march dwelt a giant, wonderly big and huge,
and he hight Moldagog: thereto was he wise and
cunning. And when they were come to the bound,
the Duke said:

"Tristram, my best friend, here is the bound of
our domain, and our domain lasteth no farther in
this wood. On the other side liveth a giant and he
dwelleth in a rock, and I do thee to wit that this
giant hath wrought me great war so that he out-
lawed me from my realm, but thereafter we made
peace betwixt us on this condition and appointment
that he should not come hither into my domain nor
I pass over the water into his domain without necessity. Now will I hold to this our pledge so long
as I may, for an I trespass against this covenant,
then hath he power to harry or burn or do whatsomever damage he may in our domain, and if he find
my men in his domain, then hath he power to slay
them. These covenants have all my noblemen sworn
to. And if any deer or hounds were to run thither
then should we lose them so that no man may drive

them home nor bring any with him. To thee also, Tristram, I forbid it to go over this water, for straightway shalt thou be spilt, shamed, and slain."

Tristram said: "God knoweth, my lord, I have no lust to go thither: I wot not what I should accomplish there. As for me, I grant this land unto him freely all my lifedays. I will have no debate with him: a forest shall not lack me whilst I live."

But therewithal he looked far within the wood and saw that the giant had the fairest trees, tall and straight and stout, and of all kinds that ever he had seen or heard named. On one side of this wood lay the sea, and on the other side no man came therein save over the stream that with a boisterous rushing ran, and therefore had they made covenant, the Duke and the giant, that no man should overpass that stream. The Duke turned him again and took Tristram's hand and they rode both together, for he was right dear unto the Duke; and they came forthwith home unto the castle and washed and sat at board, and after came the hunters home with many deer.

Chapter lxxiv

KAHERDIN and Tristram were passing good fellows: they held great war and gave hard battle unto their enemies that were in their realm and seized from them strong towns and mighty castles, for they were the boldest knights so that none was found like them. And noble princes and barons and knights submitted themselves, and these two had great power in their land and took Nantes and set their own knights in the castles that were about that people so that the mightiest men made treatise with them and sware oaths and gave them borrows and assurance of safe peace. In this mean while was Tristram in sore grief and anguish for love of Ysolt, and he devised with a right sharp wit a rede that he sought to accomplish, and it seemed him then that he had leisure therefor, for his heart and mind were all to love Ysolt and to enchieve all that he might to do her honor.

Chapter lxxv

ON a day Tristram armed him and said he would ride to chase deer away in the forest, and afterward he sent his fellows from him with the hunters. Then he let hide his chasour in a dale and took then his horn and mounted his palfrey and rode with all the speed he might thither where his destrier was and his arms, and when he had armed him as best he might he mounted his destrier and rode as fast as he might alone and came anon to the ford of the water that was the march of the Duke's land and the giant's. He saw then that the ford was perilous and ran with a great stream right deep and had banks on either side and he chose that hard jeopardy, come thereof what come might.

Then he smote his horse with the spurs and leapt him into the water, and the water came straightway over their bother heads, and he sank so heavily downwards that he thought not to escape on live. But he strove all that he might, and he came up at the last on the other side of the river, and gat from the back of his horse and reposed him a space, and took off the saddle and shook the water therefrom and from himself. When he was well rested, he mounted his horse and rode into the forest and set the horn to his mouth and blew as hard as he might and so long that the giant heard the horn. It seemed the giant marvel what that might be and he hastened forthwith thereas he heard it, and he held a great club in his hand of the hardest ebony. Whenas he beheld Tristram all armed on his horse, he asked in mickle wrath:

"Sir fool, what man art thou that sittest in arms upon thy horse? Whence art thou comen or what seekest thou here in my chase?"

Therewith answered Tristram: "I am called Tristram and am son-in-law unto the Duke of Brittany. I saw this fair wood and I thought it privy to come at and well suited to a house that I would let build, for I see here the fairest trees of all kinds, and I would let fell the strongest trees, two score and eight in number, within this fortnight."

Chapter lxxvi

WHEN the giant heard his word and understood it, then was he wroth and answered: "So defend me God, an it were not for friendship unto the Duke, I should slay thee with this club, for thou art mad with pride. Get thee forth with all the speed thou mayest from this forest, and be thou glad that I suffer thee to go forth in such case."

Then said Tristram: "Fie upon him would be glad of thy mercy. I will fell here as many trees as me liketh, and of us twain let him rule the remnant as winneth the victory."

Then said the giant in mickle wrath: "Thou art a fool and a felon and thereto swollen with pride. But on none other condition shalt thou now go forth but thou shalt give me thine head in pledge. Thou deemest me the giant Urgan that thou slewest. Nay it is not so. He was my father's brother: and he also was a kinsman that thou slewest in Spain. Now art thou come again unto Brittany to reave me of my wood. But first shalt thou have ado with me, and if thou mayest abide me, little shall thy shield cover thee when I encounter with thee."

He brandished his club and cast it at him with great strength and ire, but Tristram avoided and hasted against him to strike him, but the giant hasted to reach his club, and there was great strife betwixt them. Then Tristram leapt betwixt the giant and his club and would strike him upon the head, but as he staggered under the buffet, Tristram's sword slanted down upon his leg with so sharp a stroke that his foot fell far from him. Tristram dressed another stroke upon his head, but forthwith the giant cried on loud:

"Sir, spare my life. I will yield thee troth and surance and homage, and all my bags of treasure will I give thee, and all my land and gold that I possess shall be in thy power. I withhold naught save life only. Take me straightway whither thou wilt and as liketh thee and do with me as thou wilt."

When Tristram understood that he besought mercy, he received his submission and troth and word and sure handfast: then he made him a leg of wood and bound it under his knee, and in such wise must he follow him.

Chapter lxxvii

THE giant showed Tristram his wealth, but little regard had he thereof, for he recked not much of gain at that time, and he said unto the giant that he would not have more than him needed. When the giant was bound unto him by oath, Tristram let him possess his wealth and hold it in his castle, and they made then a new treatise that the giant would do whatsoever Tristram bade, and they were thereto accorded that Tristram should rule the wood and do therewith as him listed, and the giant promised he would tell this to no man. Then the giant yode unto the river with him and told him where he should ride over and took leave at him; and Tristram rode his ways and made such fare as he knew not what was betid, for he rode over the ford nigh the cliff and so crossed over that Kaherdin was not ware of him. He rode as fast as he might to the court and said he had gone astray all that day in the forest and had hunted a great wild boar, but he sped not to catch him, and he was sore in his bones because he gat no rest that day, and he said he had great need of rest. When he had eaten he went to sleep by his wife, and he mused much and lay waking, and Ysolt marveled much what ailed him and why he sighed so from his heart and asked him what sickness he had that he might not sleep. She asked him long with sweet and seemly words that he should tell her, but Tristram said:

"This sickness hath lain upon me sith I went in the morning into the wood and I found there a great wild boar and I dealt him two wounds with my sword and natheless he escaped me and it angered me much and thereof am I wroth and dolorous. I rode after him and he would never stand against me, and when I had done all that I might, he vanished from me into the wood at night. Now I require thee, my sweet love, that thou tell this unto no man that it be not spoken in reproach nor slander of me before my fellows or the people of the court. Great shame cometh to me of this, and when day cometh I will go unto the wood and search the whole wood: well I wot that by my honor I shall never stint ere I have caught him."

"God wot," said she, "that I shall conceal this well: heed ye well also afore other men."

And they spake no more thereof as at that time.

Chapter lxxviii

NOW Tristram rose up as soon as it dawned and rode forth privily alone and came over the river and then unto the giant's castle: and the giant kept all their covenants and purveyed him artificers and all the materials and did all as he had said afore. Where the wood was thickest was a rock round and all vaulted within, hewn and graven with the most art; and in the middes of the vault stood an arch, carved with leaves, birds, and beasts, and under each end of the arch were such strange carvings that no man living might do the like. The vault was so closed in round about that in no wise could one go in nor out of the house, save that when the sea began to ebb might one enter there with dry feet. A giant came from Africa to build this vault and dwelt there long and made war against them that were in Brittany and harried nigh all the land inhabited as far as St. Michael's Mount, that standeth on the seashore. When Arthur passed from England with his host to the Roman realm against the Emperor Lucius, the which with wrong claimed tribute of England, and when King Arthur landed up in Normandy, he heard what was fallen concerning the giant and that he did divers scathes unto men and harried nigh all the land so that the King had heard never such a marvel. He had also taken the daughter of Duke Howel and seized her with force and brought her away with him, and she was cleped Elaine: and he kept her with him in the cave and because she was a right fair woman he yearned after her with fleshly lust, but by reason of his bigness and heaviness wherewith she was strangled under him and crushed, he gat not the play that he would. Then came Duke Howel unto King Arthur and complained him of his woe and distress, and the King was full of goodwill and lamented his scathe and misadventure. And when the night came the King harnessed himself secretly and had with him II knights of his and they went to seek the giant and found him at the last: but the King alone fought him withal, and the King endured the sorest battle not without sad strokes ere he might fell the giant. But of the giant that the King slew longeth not unto this history, save only that he made this fair vaulted house that pleased Tristram as well as he might desire.

Chapter lxxix

NOW Tristram used well his puissance for to let make with much skill all manner of carvings, and he hid so cunningly his business that no man wist where he was nor wherewith he meddled him; he came thither alway early and late he returned home. He had much labor and study to bring to an end what he did, and he let wainscot all the vaulted chamber within as tightly as might be with the best wood, and let color and gild all the carvings with the most craft. Without before the door he let build the fairest hall of good timber, of which there was no lack. Then he let build about the hall a palisade for safety. In this hall worked his goldsmiths, and it was adorned all about with gold and as bright was it within as without. There were all manner of skilled craftsmen, but none of those that were there knew all Tristram's counsels, and wherefore he let build that house that divers wrights wrought with care. Tristram went so privily with his purpose that none of them knew what was his intent nor what he desired save only that which he showed the giant, that gave him gold and silver.

Chapter lxxx

NOW Tristram let hasten his wrights all that he might, and it pleased him well under the rock: woodcarvers and goldsmiths labored there and all was now accomplished and made ready unto finishing. Then Tristram suffered the wrights to go home and conveyed them till they were gone out of the island and so home unto their own land. Now hath Tristram no fellow nigh but the giant, and they bare now all the labor of the wrights and joined

together the vaulted chamber as the materials had
been afore dressed by the wrights, all colored and
gilt with the best art so that none might desire none
better. Under the middes of the vault raised they
up an image so beautiful of stature and countenance
that no man beholding it might think otherwise than
that life was in all the limbs, and so fair and so well
wrought that in all the world one might not find a
fairer image. And from the mouth arose a sweet
savor that all the chamber was filled therewith as
all the aromatic herbs that are costliest had been
there. The good savor came from the image
through this device, that Tristram had made in the
breast under the paps in place of the heart an opening, and set therein a coffer full of such herbs that
were sweetest in all the world, mingled with gold.
This image in shape and beauty and stature so re-
sembled unto Queen Ysolt as she had stood there
herself, and was so lifelike as it had been on live.
This image was so cunningly graven and so richly
clad as beseemed the noblest queen. She had on
her head a crown of pure gold wrought with all
manner of skill and set with costliest jewels and of
all colors, and in the leaf thereof that was in front
upon her forehead stood a great emerald that never
bare king nor queen its peer. In the right hand of
the image was a wand or sceptre; in the upper end
it was carved in flowers by the subtlest smiths; the
shaft of wood was all covered with gold and set
with rings of stones; the gold leaf was the best gold
of Araby: in the upper end of the wand was carved

a bird with feathers of divers colors and wrought in act to clap its wings as it had been quick and living. This image was clad in the best purple and white furs; and for this cause was she clad in purple raiment that purple tokeneth the woe and sorrow and travail and misery that Ysolt endured for the sake of her love unto Tristram. In the left hand she held her ring and there was written the words that Queen Ysolt said at their parting:

> Tristram, receive this ring in sign thou hold
> In thy remembrance sure our loves of old,
> Nor all forget the grief, the wrack, the moan
> Thou for my sake and I for thine have known.

Under her feet was a pedestal cast in laton in the likeness of that evil dwarf had slandered and accused them unto the King. The Queen's image stood upon his breast, seeming most as she trod him under her feet, and he lay under her feet crying as he were weeping. Near the image was wrought of fine gold a little plaything, her lapdog, shaking his head and ringing his bell, wrought with mickle cunning. On the other side of the dwarf stood a little image of Bringvain, the Queen's gentlewoman: she was well shapen as for her beauty and well adorned with the best apparel, and she held in her hand a hanap with a covercle, proffering it unto Queen Ysolt with a blithe visage: around the hanap were these words that said:

> Receive thou, Queen Ysolt, this brevage dark
> That erst was made in Ireland for King Mark.

[219]

On the other side of the chamber whereas one entered, Tristram had made a great image in likeness of the giant, as he were standing there himself, onelegged, and brandishing with both hands over his shoulder his club of iron, for to defend the other image. He was clad in a great goat-skin and a hairy, and the kirtle, hung scant below and he was naked below the navel and he gnashed with his teeth, and his eyes were wood as he would smite all those that came within. On the other side of the door stood a great lion, cast in laton and so cunningly fashioned that none of them that saw him deemed otherwise than he was alive. He stood on four feet and wound his tail about an image that was made after the Seneschal that slandered and accused Tristram unto King Mark. No man can show nor tell the subtlety that was in those images that Tristram let arear within the vault. And now hath he finished all that he intended in his mind and he gave it now unto the giant to rule and bade him as his thrall and servant to ward it so well that none should come nigh it, and he himself bare the keys both of the house and of the images, but the giant had all his other treasures. And it pleased Tristram well that he had thus brought the matter to an end.

Chapter lxxxi

WHEN Tristram had finished his toil he rode
home to his castle as he was wont, and ate
and drank and slept by Ysolt his wife. Right dear
was he unto his fellows, but he desired not to have
fleshly delight with his wife, and he fared so secretly that no man discovered his intent nor countenance, for all weened that he lived in wedded wise
as he should with her. And Ysolt also was so disposed that she hid it from every man and revealed
it neither unto her kindred nor friends. But when
he was away and wrought these images, her seemed
full strange where he was and what he did. In such
wise he rode home and returned again by a secret
path that none was ware of him, and came unto the
vaulted chamber, and ever when he came within before the image of Ysolt, he kissed her as oft as he
came and took her in his embrace and put his arms
about her neck as she had been on live, and with
many loving words Tristram rehearsed afore the
image [1] the joys of great love and their teen and
dolors and pains and woes. Much he kissed her
when he was blithe, but wroth was he when he was
araged what through thought or dream, what
through believing lies in his heart that she had forgotten him or that she had another lover or that she
might not avoid to love another that is more to her
will. This thought maketh him stray, and error

[1] *Here beginneth Master Thomas again.*

[221]

pursueth his heart, and he doubteth if she may not
turn her love unto fair Cariadoc. About her he is
both daily and nightly, and serveth her and flattereth and oft chideth her as touching Tristram. Tristram doubteth whether when she hath not her
desire she may not take thing that is in her power;
for that she may not have him, she may not make
another her lover. When in such anger he museth,
he showeth hatred unto the image, he will not look
upon it nor see nor speak to it. Then he bespeaketh
Bringvain and saith:

"Fair damozel, to thee I complain of the fickle-
ness and treachery that Ysolt, my love, doth unto
me."

Whatsoever he thinketh he saith unto the image:
then loseth he his assurance a little, and beholdeth
Ysolt's hand, that would reach him the golden ring,
and he seeth the cheer and the semblaunt that his
lady made him at parting and remembereth him of
the covenant made as they sundered. Then he
weepeth and crieth pardon that ever he thought such
folly and knoweth well that he is deceived of the
madness that he hath had. For this cause made he
the image that he would fain speak his heart, his
good thought and his foolish error, his pain and his
joy of love, for he knew not to whom he might discover his longing and desire. Such cheer made
Tristram in love, that oft he went and oft returned,
and oft showed fair semblaunt and oft an hard, as
I have afore mentioned. Love that setteth his heart
in error maketh him to do this: an he had not loved

Ysolt above all thing, he had not had jealousy of
another: for this cause doth he hold suspicion that
he loveth naught but her: if he had loved another
he had not been jealous of this love, but he is jealous of this because he is fearful to lose her. He
had not feared to lose her were it not for the
strength of his love, for of that which is naught
unto a man, it booteth not if it go ill or well. How
should one fear for thing that is nowise in his
thought?

Between these four is a strange love: all have
thereof anguish and dole, and one and all live in
sorrow and in none of them is there joy. First
dreadeth King Mark that Ysolt keepeth not faith
and loveth another than him: whatsoever pleasure
he enjoyeth, he suffereth care. This giveth him sore
noyance and grief in his heart, for he loveth and
desireth naught save only Ysolt, that is weary of
him. Of her body he may have his solace, but
little this sufficeth him when another possesseth her
heart, and for that is he wood and angry, and un-
ceasing is his sorrow that she loveth Tristram.
After the King, Ysolt in turn, feeleth this woe, that
she hath that which she would not and yet may not
have that she would. The King hath but one torment, but the Queen endureth it doubly. She desireth Tristram and may not enjoy him: and thereto
she must hold to her lord nor forsake nor leave
him, but of him she may have no pleasure. She
desireth neither his body nor his heart: this is one
torment that she endureth. The other is that she

desireth Tristram, yet Mark, her lord, forbiddeth that they speak not together nor may she love him. She knoweth right well there is naught under heaven that Tristram desireth so well: he desireth her and she him, yet may not have him: and this is h   sorrow. Double pain and double woe hath Sir Tristram also for her love. He is espoused v o that Ysolt that he may not love nor will not ve. Yet may he not with right forsake her: vhatsomever desire he have, he must keep her, for she will not quitclaim him. When he clippeth her, small is his joy save only for the name that she beareth: this at least comforteth him a little. For what he hath he sorroweth, but more he sorroweth for what he hath not, the fair Queen, his lady, in whom lieth his death and his life: and therefore double is the pain Tristram endureth for her, and for her love he grieveth in the arms of Ysolt as Blanches Mains, his wife. Whatsomever be the case of the other Ysolt, she hath dole without delight. She hath no pleasure of her lord and for none other hath she love: him she desireth, him she possesseth, yet of him hath she no joy. Contrary is her case to that of Mark: for he may work his will with Ysolt, albeit he may not change her heart. But the other Ysolt cannot win delight, and naught may she have save to love Tristram without delight: of him she would 'have pleasure, yet naught hath she but woe. When she would essay more than kissing and clipping, he may not yield himself nor would she ask it. Here I know not what to

say, which of them hath the greater anguish, nor
may I tell the reason, for I have not proved these
matters. I will set forth my tale: let lovers give
judgment who hath the better destiny in love, or
who had thereof the greater woe. Lord Mark
hath the body of Ysolt and hath his delight thereof
when he will: upon his heart it weigheth that she
loveth Tristram more than him, for he loveth
naught save her. Ysolt resteth in the King's power
and her body he useth as he will: of this sorrow
oft she maketh dole for unto the King she hath
no liking. It behoveth her endure it as of her lord,
but natheless she desireth not save to possess Tristram, her lover, that hath taken a wife in a strange
land. She feareth that he hath turned unto change,
but yet she hopeth that he hath no desire unto no
woman. Tristram loveth Ysolt alone and well he
knoweth that Mark, her lord, doth with her body
all his pleasure, and therefore may he have no delight save of longing and desire. A wife he hath
with whom he may not lie and whom he may not
love at such a price: naught he doth against his
heart. Ysolt as Blanches Mains, his wife may covet
naught in the world save only Tristram, her fair
lord, whose body she hath but without love: for
this cause she desireth it the more. Now he that
considereth this let him tell who fareth best in love
or who hath thereof the greatest sorrow. Ysolt as
Blanches Mains, the fair, lay with her lord, a virgin:
in one bed they slept together: I know not their joy
and their grief: but he doth never to her as to a

wife thing wherewith one may have delight. I know
not if she have aught of pleasure, nor if she loveth
or hateth thus to live, but well may I say that if it
were grievous unto her she had not hidden it as
she did from her friends.

Chapter lxxxii

IT happened that in this land Sir Tristram and Sir
Kaherdin must needs go with their neighbors to
a holy feast to pray, and Tristram brought Ysolt
with him. Kaherdin rode at her right and by his
own left rein and they went disporting them with
mirths. To their words they gave such heed that
they suffered the horses turn as they would go.
Kaherdin's horse turned aside, and that of Ysolt
reared him up and she striketh him with the spurs.
As she lifted her heels to give another stroke, she
hath need to open her legs: to hold her she gripped
with her right hand. The palfrey sprang forward
and alighting on his feet slipped in a little hole in
a pool. His hoofs were new shod and where he
went in the mire, he plunged into the hole, and as
he struck the hole, there sprang up from his hoof
water: and it splashed against her legs. She was
afeard with the cold and uttered a cry and said
naught, but from the bottom of her heart she
laughed so that if she had suffered a forty days'
penance she had scarce restrained her. Kaherdin
saw her laugh thus and weened that she had heard

somewhat noised of him wherein she noted folly or evil or villainy, for he was a meek knight and a good and a free and a lover. Therefore, had he fear of folly when he saw the laugh of his sister, and shame made him afeard. Then he began to say:

"Ysolt, ye laughed from the bottom of your heart, but I know not wherefore ye laughed. If I know not the true occasion, never shall I put trust in you, for well may ye now deceive me. If hereafter I may discover it, certes I will never yield you as unto my sister faith nor love."

Ysolt heard that he said and wist that if she hid this from him he would have right evil will unto her and said: "I laugh for my thought of an adventure, and therefore I laugh when I remember me of it. This water which splashed up hath been more bold than ever was Tristram. Brother, now have I told you [1] wherefore I laughed."

Then forthwithal Kaherdin answered with swift words: "Ysolt, what is this ye say? Have ye not slept together with Tristram in one bed as in hallowed wedlock? What doth he then that he liveth as a monk and ye as a nun? Uncourteously he hath used you if he played not with you?"

Ysolt said: "Never played he with me save only that he kisseth me, and seldom that save when we go to bed. Never have I known man more than I had been a maid that hath lived most cleanly."

Then said Kaherdin: "I deem, then, that rather it liketh him to have his lust of others rather then

[1] *Here Brother Robert again taketh up the tale.*

[227]

to have your maidenhead and that he must desire others. Had I known this, he had never entered your bed."

Then said Ysolt: "No man may missay him of this. I trow he may give another reason, and for that he liveth thus I will not that ye blame him of it."

Chapter lxxxiii

WHEN Kaherdin was assured of this that his sister was a virgin, he was right wroth, and he mused and him seemed as this were a shame unto them both and unto all his kindred. In this sorrow he rode on and said naught at all as at this time by reason of those that followed them, and they came within a while to this holy place for to make their orison. So when they had done as behoved them, they returned unto their horses and rode home, making mirth. Then was Kaherdin ill disposed toward Tristram, his fellow, and he would not speak of the matter with him; and Tristram had marvel what should have caused it that he showed him such strangeness when afore he told him all things both before and after, and Tristram was wroth in heart and he thought whether he might come to know of this and what he found to blame. And on a day Tristram said unto him:

"Fellow, how fareth it now? Have I wronged thee in anything? I behold in thee great malice

din more than any other friend and therefore would
he by no mean anger him more; yet he doubted that
if he told him he might tell his sister, yet if he spake
not, then was he lost and perished, betrayed and
shent, were it with right or were it with wrong, for
surely might Kaherdin with some shift compass his
death. Then he said:

"Kaherd my best friend, it is thou hast made
me to know this realm, and by thy counsels have I
won me many honors, and if I have done thee mischief, then well ma thou do me hurt if thou wilt
meddle thee therein. But of my will and of my
power will I not cause anger and strife between us
through no deed that I may perform, though it be
much against my desire. Now th thou wilt know
mine intent and loves and priv that no man
knoweth but I alone, and if thou see a fair
damozel and her conversation and nt, and
nobley and semblaunt, then I require of th y thy
fellowship that thou break not this secret my
privy speech unto thy sister nor none other, to by
no mean would I that she should know nor ne
other."

Then answered Kaherdin: "See here my suranc
and oath that never will I disclose that thou wilt
have secret, and of me shall no man learn this but
if thou shalt deem it counsel and so tell me hereafter."

Now gave each of them to other troth and loyalty
to hold the secret that Tristram should tell him.

Chapter lxxxv

ON a morning right early they made ready their going secretly and all they that abode in the town wondered where it was their purpose to go. But Tristram and Kaherdin went forthwith their ways while the day dawned, and rode through woods and wildernesses and came to the ford, and Tristram made as he would ride over the water, and when he was gone down into the ford, Kaherdin cried with a loud voice:

"Tristram, what wilt thou essay?"

Tristram answered: "I would ride across the water and show thee that I have promised thee."

Then was Kaherdin wroth and said: "Thou wouldst betray me and bring me into the power of the giant, my greatest foe, that slayeth all that go there. Thou wouldst do this for thou wouldst not hold thy foreward that thou hast sworn unto me. If we cross the water, never shall we return on live."

When Tristram heard that, he was wroth, and blew his horn as loud as he might IV times: in this wise he gave a sign to the giant to come thither. Then came the giant on the other bank upon the rock as wroth as he were wood, and brandished his iron club, and called Tristram with a dreadful voice and said:

"What wilt thou with me that thou callest me so strongly?"

Tristram answered: "I bid thee to suffer this

knight to follow me whithersoever I will, and to cast away thine iron club."

He did so straightway. Then Kaherdin took courage and rode over the water to Tristram, and Tristram told him of their battle, how they had foughten and he had hewn off the giant's leg. Then they rode their ways and came to the rock and they alight from their horses and went within the courtelage, and Tristram opened the house, and straightway sprang to them the sweet savor of balsam and of all the sweetest grasses that were there. Wh Kaherdin espied the face of that giant at t door, he was so afeard that nigh h gone out of his wit, for he m had betrayed him and that t e giant would slay him with his brandished cl But of this fear and of the odor that was ir he house he had such marvel that he fell in a swoon. Tristram raised him up and said unto h a:

"Enter we here, for here is the damozel that serveth the noble lady that I mentioned unto thee and that I heartily love."

But Kaherdin was all in fear and dread and seemed as he were frenzied in his mind and had lost his reason: he beheld the image of the giant and he deemed it living. But Tristram went unto the image of Ysolt and embraced her and kissed her and spake low and whispered in her ear and murmured as it had been she that much he loved, and he said unto the image:

"My fairest lady, thy love maketh me sick both

night and day, for all my longing and all my desire accord unto thy longing and thy desire."

At whiles was he right sad and dolorous of his speech, and at whiles he made as he were of blithe cheer.

Chapter lxxxvi

THEN seemed it a great marvel to Kaherdin and he said: "Tristram, behoveth me somewhat to win where so fair women be. I see that ye have the fairest leman: make me to share in your pleasures that I may be the lover of the queen's gentlewoman. If ye hold not foreward with me that ye promised me, ye shall have shame thereof when we go home."

Then Tristram took him by the hand and led him unto the image of Bringvain and said: "Is not this maid fairer than Ysolt, your sister? And if it should fortune that this matter get about, let this that here ye may see bear witness."

Then answered Kaherdin: "I see, indeed, that these be fairer; and therefore behoveth you to share with me their beauty: so long have we been fellows it beseemeth us be partakers of these twain."

"Yea," said Tristram, "I choose the Queen, and take ye the maid; I yield her thee."

Then answered Kaherdin: "God thee thank that thou usest me so well. Such is token of friendship and fellowship."

He saw a golden cup in her hand and weened it had been full of wine and would take it from her, but the cup was nailed and fastened with such cunning that he might nowise take it, and he considered it then carefully, and saw that it was but an image of both, and said unto Tristram:

"A wily man art thou and full of craft that thou hast deceived me thus much and beguiled me, that am thy steadfast friend and dear fellow. But if ye show me not those after which these been made, ye have made a lie of all our foreward: but an ye show me the creatures that be like these in semblaunt and beauty, then are ye true of your promise and I may trust your words, and then would I that ye grant me the living damozel as ye have given me the image."

Then said Tristram: "It shall surely be an ye will hold your word with me."

And they bound their covenant betwixt them with a new surance and true knighthood. Then Tristram showed him all that was there painted and carven, gilt and chiseled with such divers cunning that never erst saw man's eye the like, and Kaherdin wondered in what wise Tristram had brought all this to an end. Thereupon Tristram closed the house and they returned home. When they had rested at home a few days, they each made ready to visit holy places and they took staffs and scrips and had no man with them but two of their kin, fair men and strong and bold in arms and gentle after the manner of courts. All their armor they took with

them and they said to the courtiers and all the folk
that they took their harness with them for that they
feared outlaws and wicked men in foreign lands.
Then they took leave at their friends and went their
ways [1] and went straight into England for to see
Ysolt and seek Bringvain, for her would Kaherdin
behold and Tristram would behold again Ysolt.

Chapter lxxxvii

WHAT availeth it to lengthen the tale or tell
that is of no force? I will rehearse but the
sum and fine thereof. Tristram and Kaherdin have
ridden and wandered till that they came unto a city
where Mark was to lie that night, and when Tristram heard that he was to come there he goeth
forth against him with Kaherdin for he knew the
road: far sundered they went, watching for the
King's company. When the King's meynie was
passed, they met the Queen's. Then they withdrew
them from the road thereas their squires abode them.
Then have they mounted upon an oak that stood
over the paved road, where they may survey the
train, but it may not perceive them. There come
boys, there come varlets, there come hounds and
brachets, couriers and keepers of the hounds, kit-
chen-knaves and kennel-boys, marshals and har-
bingers: lo now, sumters and chasours, lo now,
destriers and palfreys led by the hand, lo, birds

[1] *Here Master Thomas taketh up the story.*

carried upon the left fist. Great is that company upon the road. Much Kaherdin marveleth him of the company that is so great and of the wonders that are so many and that he seeth not the Queen nor Bringvain, the fair maiden. Behold now the laundresses and the common chamberers that serve the business of undoing and dressing the beds, of sewing clothes and washing hair and looking to other matters. Then said Kaherdin:

"Now I espy her."

"Nay," said Tristram, "ye do not, by the faith of my body. These be but the common chamberers, that do the rough labor."

Lo now, the chamberlains. After them spread the rows of knights and damozels, well nurtured and brave and fair. They sing fair song and pastourelles. Then come the damozels, daughters of princes and lords, born of divers regions. They sing joyous songs and ballads. With them come the amorous knights, well faren and valiant, that speak as they go of druery and of true love. Then said Kaherdin:

"Now I see her. She in front is the Queen: and which is Bringvain the maid?"[1]

"That is not she," said Tristram; "these be but the least of her tiring women."

At the last came Ysolt and Bringvain riding, and each held a dog in her arms. Tristram sighed from his heart and might scarce restrain him. But

[1] *Here I follow the tale which, as men say, Thomas of Erceldoune endited in English.*

[237]

Kaherdin looked as he were astonied because of the marvelous beauty of the Queen Ysolt and of her maiden, Bringvain.

"Tristram, my friend," said he, "nothing hast thou lied to me, nor were the images half so fair as be these living ladies. My sister is not worthy to be the maiden of thy lady's maiden."

When they were passed, Tristram said: "Kaherdin, draw this ring from off my finger and ride after and greet these ladies. Praise the dog Petitcru and stroke him, and the Queen will know the ring thou wearest, and she will ask whence thou hast it."

Then rode Kaherdin and overtook them: first he saluted the Queen and after Bringvain, and asked where he might find harborage. He stroked the dog Petitcru, and forthwith the Queen saw the ring and waxed all pale, for well she knew it for Tristram's. She said:

"Tell me, fair sir, how came this ring to you?"

He answered privily: "He that oweth the ring sent it you for a token."

And privily she answered: "By God, long have we waited in sorrow and woe for him." Then openly she said: "Ride on, stranger knight and get you harborage in the next castle, nor delay our traveling."

So when the train was wholly passed, Tristram and Kaherdin join their squires and ride forth after the King's court and the Queen, and they had knowledge of whither they should go.[2] The King came

---

[2] *Here again Brother Robert telleth the tale.*

unto that castle where he should harbor him that night, and when the King and Queen had eaten and drunken in noble wise, the Queen feigned that she was sore sick and they weened she would die. So they ordered it that she would sleep that night in a pavilion without the castle with her gentlewoman Bringvain and a maid that served them: but the King slept in another chamber that night with his faithful men. Now when the King was fallen on sleep and all his meynie, the Queen lay in a secret wood nigh unto the castle. Tristram and Kaherdin bade their squires abide there and heed their horses and arms till they came again, and they went disguised unto the castle for to wit where the harborage of the Queen was, and they went thither secretly and knocked on the door. Queen Ysolt sent her maiden to wit whether some poor men were comen there to seek alms, and when the maiden opened the door, Tristram bowed before her, saluting her with blithe words and took straightway the ring that Ysolt had given him and bade her take it unto her. Ysolt sighed and knew it straightway, and Tristram led Kaherdin into that hostel, and right so Tristram caught Ysolt and kissed her with exceeding joy and bliss. Kaherdin yode then unto Bringvain, halsing her and kissing her lovingly. When they had don: so a long while, a drink was brought unto them with all manner dainties. Then went they to bed, and that same night Kaherdin took his lady Bringvain with great love in his embrace. But she took a silk cushion wrought with marvelous craft and cunning

and laid it under his head, and forthwithal he fell
on sleep and awoke not all that night: thus slept
they together that night, Kaherdin and Bringvain.
And Kaherdin woke not till the morn and looked
then about him and wist not where he was become.
When he was ware that Bringvain was risen, he
understood that he was deceived for that he awoke
so late. Ysolt began to make mirth of that craft
and to mock him, but he was right wroth against
Bringvain, but little did he disclose it, and they were
all together that day with great pleasaunce. That
night went they to sleep and Bringvain put Kaherdin
to sleep then in the same wise as tofore, and when
the day was come he awoke in the same wise. The
third night Ysolt would not on Kaherdin's half that
he be deceived longer, and their union came to pass
with mickle joy. So long time were they all together in great love that they were discovered in
their works by their foes, but it was told them
afore, and Tristram and Kaherdin took heed and
went forth privily, but they might not come unto
their arms and horses.

Chapter lxxxviii

FOR Cariadoc had first discovered their horses.
But Tristram's squires, which watched over
their horses, were ware of what was befallen and
fled away and bare the shields and arms of their
masters, and they heard behind them the cries and

noise of them that pursued them. Cariadoc, that was nighest them, saw the squires fleeing and weened it had been Tristram and Kaherdin, and cried on high saying:

"By no means shall ye escape, for this day shall ye lose your life and here shall ye leave your bodies in pledge. Fie on such knights to flee neither for peril nor for death. Do ye not come from your lemans? Wit ye well ye shame them with great shame."

With such words spake Cariadoc, but the squires let the horses run all they might. When Cariadoc would no more pursue them, he and his men turned them again to deal with the Queen and Bringvain, her gentlewoman, and when they had long reproached them for the sake of Tristram and Kaherdin, Cariadoc began to bemock Bringvain, saying:

"This night was in thy bed the knight most coward and the most recreant that hath walked in the world: well it beseemeth thee to love such a lover as fleeth from knights as a hare from hounds! I cried him many times with many words and a loud voice that he should abide me and have ado with me, and he durst not look behind him. Shamefully hast thou set thy love that thou grantest it to such a caitiff, and thou hast brought thy love down unto a knight coward, and so hast thou been ever deceived and led astray, and never more may I show thee my love with my goodwill."

Chapter lxxxix

WHEN Bringvain had heard so many scornful words, she said in great wrath: "Be he fearle or afeard, I choose him to my lover rather than thy alse beauty. God grant that never he may have victor over none if he be not more braver than thou. Certes, he showed him recreant if afore thee he fled, nd thou darest not slander him, for many men find more to scorn in thee. For that thou speakest ag inst him touching his flight, may it hap by God's w that thou shalt have true knowledge whether he w'l flee before thee or no. Got wot that I may nev r believe that he fled before thee nor that thou du t look upon him even with wrath or malice. Kaher n is a man so bold and mighty and so good knight hat he would flee never afore thee more than gre, und afore an hare, or lion afore a goat."

Then answered Cariac c: "They fled as cowards both, or else where is th Kaherdin become? He hath a shield all new gilt and all depainted with leaves, and his horse is dapple gray, and if I espy him another time I shall know his spear and his cognizance both."

Then Bringvain understood that Cariadoc knew his shield and cognizance, horse and armour,[1] and she was woe and wroth, and departed from him in

[1] *Here Master Thomas taketh up the story unto the end.*

anger, and yode thereas she found Ysolt, that for
Tristram made dole in her heart.

"Lady," said Bringvain, "I am but dead. To
my harm did I see the hour when I knew you, you
and Tristram your lover both. Wholly I left my
land for you and for your light heart lost I my
maidenhood. I did it, certes, for your great love:
ye promised me great honor, ye and Tristram, the
trothbreaker, wherefor may God yield him misfor-
tune and heavy hardship in his life. For his sake
was I first shamed. Remember you when ye sent me
forth and gave commandment to destroy me: it came
not of your truth that of your thralls I was not slain.
Their hate more availed me than your love. Caitiff
and accursed was I when I believed you that hour
or that ever I had love to you sith I had nigh known
death through you. Wherefore have I not sought
your death sith ye sought mine with wrong? This
mischief had I all forgiven, but now is it renewed
by the treason and malengine which ye have wrought
and Kaherdin. Fie upon your noblesse when thus
ye requite my service. Is this, lady, the great worship ye have granted me for my love? He would
but have company wherewith to work his lust.
Ysolt, ye have caused this be done to draw me unto
folly, and shame have ye done me, lady, to please
your malice. Ye have set me in disworship, and
thereby is our love destroyed. Ah, God, how have
I heard you praise him to make me enamored of
him. Never was man of his noblesse and of his pris
and of his valor! What a knight did ye make him!

Ye h, 'd him for best man of the world, but he is the m. t dastard that ever bore shield or brand. Sith th. he fled before Cariadoc, may his body be shamed (d perished: sith that he fled for so evil a man, gre. ter recreant is there none betwixt here and Rome. Now tell me, Queen Ysolt, sith when have ye been Richolt? Where have ye learned her art to prai: thus an evil man and to betray a miserable woman ' Wherefore have ye so shamed me with the man lost coward of this earth? So many brave men hav come to woo me, and against them all have I guarde 1 me, and now am I delivered unto a coward. This v as by your enticement, and I will have vengeance o. ou and of Tristram, your lover. Ysolt, you and hu. do I defy both. With evil will I seek you and wit. mischief by reason of this my foul shame."

Chapter xc

WHEN Ysolt heard this woman enchafed and heard this defiance from her u. at most she trusted in and that best ought to keep her honor, for she that spake so vilely such filth was her solace and joy, she was so deeply stricken in heart that she was wroth with her and near her heart the wrath came. Two pains took hold on her spirit; she knew not from whom to defend her nor with whom she might take refuge. She sighed and said:

"Unhappy and wretch am I. Great grief is it

[244]

that I live so long, for never heard I such evil name in this foreign land. Tristram, may your body be accursed: by you am I comen in such distress: ye brought me to this land, and in pain have I ever been here. For your sake have I debate with my lord and all them of this land, privily and openly. Who recketh him thereof? Well have I endured it and still might I endure it an I had the love of Bringvain. When she would purchase me harm and hateth me, I know not what to 'do. She was wont to maintain my joy, but for your sake now would she shame me. To my sorrow learnt I ever your love, so much wrath and anger have I. Ye have wrested from me all my kin and the love of all this strange people. All this seemeth me but a little thing, if ye take not away from me at the last all the solace I have, to wit, the noble Bringvain. So brave and so loyal was damozel never, but between you and Kaherdin ye have 'drawn her away by craft. Ye would take her with you to wait upon Ysolt as Blanches Mains: because ye know her loyal, ye would have her about your wife: toward me ye 'do as a traitor when ye take from me my fosterling. Bringvain, remember thee of my father and of my mother's prayer. If thou forsake me here in a strange land without a friend, what shall I do? What way shall I live, for of none have I solace? Bringvain, if ye would desert me, ye ought not to hate me for this cause, nor to seek occasion against me for to go to another realm. For a good farewell would I give you an ye went with Kaherdin.

Well know I that Tristram maketh you to do this, to whom may God give therefor great damage."

Bringvain heareth Ysolt's speech, nor might she refrain her of speaking and said:

"Ye have a fell heart when ye say such outrage of me and that which I have never thought. Tristram ought not to be blamed. But ye should have the disworship sith ye have enjoyed him unto your power. Had ye not desired the evil thing, ye had not enjoyed him so long. The lechery that ye so love, would ye turn upon Tristram, albeit if Tristram had not been, ye had enjoyed the love of a worse man than he. Of his love I complain not, but I have great grief and woe that ye have beguiled me to consent to your sin. Shent am I if ever I consent thereto more. Keep you well from this time, for of you I think to be well avenged. If ye had list that I should marry, why gave ye me not to a man chivalrous? But by your engine have ye given me to the most dastard that was born ever."

Ysolt answered: "Your pardon, my friend, never did I felony unto you, nor for harm nor for wickedness was this counsel made. So God me help, I did it for good intent. Kaherdin is a good knight and a rich duke and a trusty warrior. Think not that he fled for that he feared Cariadoc: rather it is said of envy, for never had he fled for him. If ye hear lies of him, ye ought not therefore to hate Tristram, my lover, nor me. Bringvain, I ensure you by the faith of my body, howsoever your rede fall out, that all they of this court would rejoice at our strife and

our enemies will have glee thereof. If ye have
hatred unto me, who then will wish me honor? How
may I be honored if I be reviled of you? By none
may one be more deeply betrayed then by his fa-
miliars and fosterlings. When a familiar knoweth
a man's counsel, well may he betray him if he hate
him. Bringvain, ye that know all my fare, if
it please you, ye may indeed shame me. But this
will be a reproach unto you if, when ye had me in
your counsel, ye should for malice discover my
counsel and my secret to the King. On the contrary,
I have done this thing for thy sake: there should
be no evil will betwixt us: our wrath is of no avail.
Never did I this unto thy shame, but unto thy great
weal and honor. Forgive me thy hate.

"Wherein shalt thou be advantaged an I were
in disgrace with the King? Certes, in my dishonor
will not be your advantage; rather if I be defamed
by thee, thou shalt be the less esteemed and loved:
no man will be able to praise thee that doth not
thereby reproach thee. Thou wilt rather be despised of all well-taught folk, and thou wilt have
lost my love and my lord's friendship. Whatsoever
countenance he maketh me, think not that he will
not hate thee: to me hath he so great love that
never might he set his hate upon me. No man
might so divide us that he might sunder his body
from me. My deeds he may hold in loathing, but
me he may not hate for no good: my follies he may
hate, but he may not forsake my love: my deeds
he may hate in his heart, but whatsomever he may

de. re else, he must needs love me. Never to none
that bare me evil will, came good of the King. They
that ell him thing that most he hateth, wit ye well
he be reth them evil will. What wilt thou advantage t e King if thou missay me unto him? Of
what v uldst thou be avenged if thou shouldst work
me har 1? Wherefore wouldst thou betray me?
What lt thou discover unto him? That Tristram can ? to speak with me? What damage had
the King hereof? Wherein shalt thou advantage
him if thou make him to hold me in despite? I know
not what th ng he hath lost."

Bringvair aid: "Thou art forbidden, and thereto
hast thou n le avow, a year agone, not to speak
with nor to ve Tristram. That command and
that oath has hou kept right ill. Unto thy power,
wretched Ysol thou art forsworn and a faith-
breaker and a r. Thou art so used to evil thou
mayst not forsak : it: thou must hold to thine old
custom. An thou hadst not been used thereto from
thy childhood, th wouldst not continue to do it:
an thou delighted ot so in sin thou wouldst not
hold it long. Wi t thing a colt learneth in the
breaking, will he nill he, long it endureth; and what
thing a woman learr th in youth, if she have not
chastisement, it endu h all her life days if her
power accord unto her desire. Evil hast thou learnt
in thy youth, and all thy days will it be thine intents: an thou hadst not learnt in youth, thou hadst
not used it so long. An the King had punished thee,
thou hadst not done wickedness, but sith that he

hath assented him thereto, thou has used it thus long. But he hath suffered it because he hath never been certain: I will tell him the sooth, and then will he do his will. So much hast thou been hardened in love thou hast forgotten honor and wrought such folly thou wilt not leave it the term of thy life. After that the King apperceived it, of right ought he to have punished thee: now so long hath he suffered it, he is among all his people shamed. Behoved him to carve off thy nose or otherwise deal with thee that always thou hadst been shamed. Great shame wert thou to thy friends. He ought to have done thee shame when thou wert dishonoring thy lineage, thy friends and thy lord. An thou hadst not lost thine honor, thou hadst left thy wickedness. Well wot I wherein thou trustest; in the King's kindness, that sufferest all thy desires. Therefore he will not hate thee, nor wilt thou leave of thy shame. To thee he hath so great love that he endureth his disworship, but if he had not loved thee so, so had he punished thee. I will not forbear, Ysolt, for to tell thee, thou dost great villainy and shame to thy body when he loveth thee so sore and thou bearest thee toward him as unto a man thou lovest not. Hadst thou love to him, thou hadst not wrought him this dishonor."

When Ysolt heard herself so missaid, she answered Bringvain with heat: "Ye judge me too cruelly. Fie upon your judgment! Ye speak as one ill-nurtured when ye hold me for so disloyal. Certes, an I be a faith-breaker and perjurer or shamed in some thing or have done villainy, ye have well counseled me therein. Had ye not been consenting, never had folly been betwixt Tristram and me. But for that ye consented, ye have learned me what I should do. The great crafts and woes, the fears and sorrows and the love that we have maintained, through you were they done when we did them. Ye indeed first deceived me, then Tristram, and then the King, for it is long he had known it, had he not been deceived by you. By the lies ye spake ye maintained us in our folly, and by craft and subtlety did ye cover our works. More are ye to blame than I, sith that it behoved you to keep me: but rather ye accomplished my shame. Now would ye discover the wickedness that I have done under thy governance. Evil were I and may an evil flame consume me if, when one shall come to tell him the truth, I conceal aught on my party: and then if the King shall take vengeance, of you will he take it first, and well have ye deserved it of him. Natheless, I cry you mercy that ye discover not this secret and pardon me of your wrath."

Then said Bringvain: "Now, by my faith, will I do it, and will show it forthwith to the King. We shall hear which hath the wrong and which the right. Let hap what happen may."

In malice she parteth straight from Ysolt and sweareth she will tell the King of it. In this wrath and this anger goeth Bringvain to speak her desire unto the King.

"Sire," saith she, "now hearken, and what I shall

say believe ye for truth." With secret purpose she rehearseth all before the King, and with a great subtlety is she fulfilled. She saith: "Hearken me short space. Fealty and faith I owe you, and loyalty and firm love unto your person and your honor, and when I speak of you shame, meseemeth I may not conceal it, and if I had known it afore, certes I had discovered it. Of Ysolt thus much would I say: she demeaneth her worse than she is wont: she is corrupt of heart and if she be not better watched, she will do folly of her body; for never yet hath she done it, but she waiteth but a convenient season. For no cause had ye erst suspicion at her. But now have I had great wrath and dread of heart and fear because she will not tarry for naught an she may enchieve her will. Therefore I come to counsel you that ye let watch her better. Have ye heard ever the saying: 'Empty chamber maketh light lady, easy taking maketh thief, light lady maketh empty house.' Long have ye been in error: I myself was in doubt, and night and day I watched her. But meseemeth I have done it for naught, for we have been deceived in error and thought: she hath beguiled us in all things and changed the dice without casting them. Let us now beguile her in casting the dice, that she arrive not to her intents nor have her will, however much she desireth it. For if one should restrain her a little, I believe she will withdraw her therefrom. Certes, Mark, of right ought shame to befall you if ye assent you to all her pleasures and suffer her lover to be about her. I wot right well

I do but as a fool that I spake word to you of this, for ye will hold me in evil favor: but now know ye well the sooth. What semblaunt soever ye make, I know despite your feigning, ye have not the power to dare to do your semblaunt. King, I have told you enough, together with that ye know already."

The King listeneth the language of Bringvain and hath great marvel that this may be that she should make mention of his fear and of his shame that he hath suffered, and that she should know that he feigned, what semblaunt soever he made. Then is he in great amazement and prayeth her that she tell him the truth, for he had weened that Tristram was in the Queen's chamber as he had wont. Faithfully he giveth his affiance that he will never tell her counsel. Then said Bringvain with mickle cunning:

"My King, on pain of losing all my service, I would not hide the love nor the crafts that she hath devised. We have been deceived by the error that we made, that unto Tristram she bare her love. But she hath a richer love, that is to say, Earl Cariadoc. Of him cometh your shame: so oft hath he required Ysolt of her love that now meseemeth she is willing to grant it: so hath he flattered and served her that she would make him her lover. But of this I plight you my faith that he hath had never more of her than of me. I say not that if he found good occasion, he might not do all his will, for fair is he and full of treason: he is about her both morn and eve and serveth her and flattereth. No marvel were it an she should work folly with a rich man and so

[252]

amorous. My King, I marvel much of you that ye endure him so much about her and for what cause ye love him so much. Tristram only ye fear, but unto him she hath no love: well have I perceived it: we were deceived both. Sith he hath come to England to seek your land and your love and Ysolt heard speech thereof, she hath had men for to wait upon him to slay him: it is she hath sent Cariadoc to fleme him with force: truly we know not when she did it, but of Ysolt came this bushment. But wit ye well an she had ever loved him, she had not purchased him such disworship. If he be dead, it is great sin, for he is valiant and well-conditioned and is your nephew, Sir King. Never will ye have better friend."

When the King heareth these tidings, all his heart wavereth thereat, for he knoweth not what he should do. He will not publish this language for he wot no profit thereof. To Bringvain he saith privily:

"Friend, this deed beseemeth you well. For your sake will I not meddle save that as fairly as I may I shall banish Cariadoc and ye shall have the charge of Ysolt. Suffer her no secret communication of baron nor knight that ye be not thereat. I betake her to your care: may she henceforth be your charge."

Now is Ysolt under the hand and the counsel of Bringvain, and nothing she doth nor sayeth privily that Bringvain is not at the speaking. Tristram and Kaherdin go their ways sorrowing and mourning. Remaineth Ysolt in great grief and Bringvain, which sore complaineth. Mark on his party hath a heart right heavy and is in sorrow of his error. ~ariadoc dwelleth in great pain, the which paineth h. n for love of Ysolt, but may not speed with her to 'ield him her love, nor will he accuse her unto the King. Now Tristram began to consider how that i departed like a churl when he wist not what nor h it was with Queen Ysolt nor what Bringvain the free did. He commended Kaherdin to God and eturned all the way and vowed that never would he t happy until he had approved their estate. Might 'y was Tristram seized of love, for now he did on poo weeds, foul clothing, and wretched attire that no m nor woman might know nor perceive that he w Tristram. He deceived all by an herb wherewith made his visage swell and puff as he had a meas To hide him surely he made twist his feet and h ds. He appareled him as he had been a lazar, an thereto he took a wooden hanap the Queen gave im the first year he loved her, and he set in it a eat ball of boxwood and thus he made him a cla er. Then he repaired him unto the King's court d drew nigh unto the gate and much he longed to ow and see the condition of the court. Often he rayed and often he rattled, but he might not hear tidings whereof he should be right glad of heart.

Chapter xci

ON a day the King held a feast and yode unto
the high church for to hear the service, and
he issued forth from the palace and the Queen after
him. Tristram saw her and prayed her of largess,
but Ysolt knew him not: he followed her and rattled
and with a loud voice he cried to her, beseeching
her piteously for God's love of her great compas-
sion to give him of her goods. Thereof great
mockage made the sergeants that followed the
Queen: one thrust him, another pushed him, and
they drave him from the way. One threatened him,
another smote him, but he went on and besought
them for God's sake to do him some kindness, and
he turned not away for no threating. All held him
for a noyance; they wist nothing how he was constrained thereto. He followed within the chapel
and cried and rattled with his hanap. Ysolt was
sore annoyed withal and looked on him as a woman
enchafed and marveled what he had that he so drew
him anigh her. She espied the hanap that she knew,
and then she understood well that it was Tristram
by his gentle body, by his fashion, and by the form
of his stature. She is afeard in her heart and
changeth the color of her visage, for she hath great
dread of the King. A ring of gold she taketh from
her finger, but wot not by what mean she might
give it him, and she would throw it in his hanap.
While she held it in her hand, Bringvain avised her

[255]

thereof and looked at Tristram and knew him and perceived his engine. She told him he was a fool and a sot for to throw him upon barons, and she called the sergeants knaves that they suffered him among people that were whole and said to Ysolt that she feigned:

"Sith when have ye been so holy that ye would give so largely to a sick man or a poor? Would ye give him your ring? By the faith of my body, lady, ye shall not do this. Give not so great fee or ye will repent you of it after, and if ye give it him now, this day will ye repent you."

Unto the sergeants that she saw nigh hand she commanded that he be set without the church, and they set him without the door, and Tristram durst not beg more. And now perceived he well and knew that Bringvain hated him and Ysolt, and for this cause he knew not what to do: in his heart he had right sore anguish, for right felonously had she bidden drive him away. From his eyes the water ran right tenderly and he bemoaned his fortune and his youth, that ever he had set all his mind on love. Such woes hath he endured, such pains, such fears, such anguish, such perils, such misease, such exile he might not cease of his weeping. There was now an old palace in the court and it was ruinous and fallen in sunder and under the steps thereof Tristram hid him. He made great dole of his misease and great pain and of his life that he led. Right feeble was he of travail and fasting and waking: of his great travail and labor Tristram languished under the steps and desired his death and hated his life and never might he arise without aid. Thereto was Ysolt right pensive and bewailed herself for sorrowful and wretched that she had seen depart the thing that most she loved. She wist not what to do and wept and sighed full oft and cursed the day and cursed the hour that she tarried so long in the world.

Chapter xcii

THEY heard the service in the minster and then went unto the palace to eat and to use all the day in mirth and glee, but Ysolt had thereof no delight. It fortuned that against night the porter became right cold in the lodge thereas he sat, and he said to his wife that she should go seek wood and fetch it. The dame list not to go far and under the steps might she find dry wood and old staves and thither she went and tarried not. She entered in the darkness and came upon Tristram there asleep and found his shaggy cloak. She shrieked and well nigh she went out of her wit and she weened it had been a devil, for she wist not what he was. In her heart she was sore adread, and she came and spake to her husband. He went unto the waste hall and lit a candle and found Tristram lying there, the which was already nigh to the death. He marveled what creature it might be and came nearer with the candle and was ware of his form, that it was a man's shape. He found him colder than ice and asked who he was and what he did and what way he came under the steps. Tristram showed him all his plight and the occasion wherefor he came unto that house, and Tristram put great affiance in him and the porter loved him. With mickle toil and somedele pain he led him unto his lodge and made him a soft bed to lie on and sought him drink and victuals. He bare Tristram's message unto Ysolt and Bringvain: but for naught that he might say might Tristram find grace with Bringvain.

Chapter xciii

Y'SOLT called Bringvain unto her and said: "Gentle damozel, Tristram and I both cry thee mercy. Go, speak to him, I pray thee, and comfort him in his woe: he dieth for anguish and grief. Once thou wast wont to love him much: fair friend, go solace him now. He desireth naught but thee only. Tell him at least the cause wherefor thou hatest him and sith what time."

Bringvain said: "To none avail thou speakest: never shall he have comfort of me. I wish him rather death than life or health. This year will I not be chidden that through me thou hast done folly: no more will I hide thy villainy. Foully did he depart from us because that through me thou hast done all and through my false feigning was your work wont to be covered. Thus alway is he faren withal that felon serveth: or early or late he loseth his travail. I have served you unto my power: and for this forsooth I deserve your malice. An thou hadst regard to my bounty, thou hadst rendered me other service and other reward of my pain than to shame me with such a lord."

Ysolt said: "Be it so. Thou shouldst not rebuke me for that I said in wrath: certes, it grieveth me that I did it. I pray thee pardon me and hie thee unto Tristram, for never will he have joy if he have not speech with thee of this matter."

So she flattereth and so she prayeth and so she promiseth and so she beseecheth her mercy that Bringvain goeth to speak with Tristram to recomfort him in the lodge there he lieth. She findeth him sick and full feeble, pale of face, weak of body, meagre of flesh, and discolored. She seeth that he groaneth and how he sigheth tenderly and prayeth her piteously that she say for God's love wherefore she holdeth him in hatred and that she tell him sooth. He ensured her that it was no sooth what she had put upon Kaherdin and that he will make him come unto the court for to give Cariadoc the lie. Bringvain believed him and received his faith, and so they made accordment, and went then unto the Queen above in a chamber of marble. With great love weren they accorded and they comforted their sorrows. Tristram had pleasaunce of Ysolt, and after long space of the night he took his leave at the dayspringing, and so departed into his country and found his kinsman that awaited him and passed over

the sea with the first wind and came unto Ysolt of
Brittany, which was dolorous of this deed. Her
love weareth her to the bone, and in her heart she
had mickle grief and heaviness and woe. All his
voyage long was she tormented that he loved the
other Ysolt. This was the cause whereof she made
dole.

Now is Tristram departed. Queen Ysolt abideth,
the which complaineth her for love of Tristram,
that he goeth in such evil case: she knoweth not
surely how he fareth. For the great harms that he
hath suffered, which privily he hath discovered to
her, for the pain and the woe that he hath had for
her love, for his anguish and for his grief, she would
fain share his sorrow. Even as she hath shared in
Tristram's love, that hath languished for her, so
would she share eke in Tristram's woe and anguish.
For him she heedeth many matters that war upon
her beauty and leadeth her life in sorrow; and she,
that is a lover true in her thought and in her great
sighs and torn much by her desires, so that never
was more loyal lady seen, doth on a corselet upon
her bare flesh; there she weareth it, night and day,
save when she lieth by her lord: and men perceive
it not at all. A vow she maketh and an oath that
never would she remove it but if she knew Tristram's estate. Right sore penance she suffereth for
her love by many deeds, and much pain and anguish
Ysolt suffereth for Tristram, and misease and woe
and distress. Thereafter she took a fiddler, and
through him she sent Tristram all her life and all

her estate, and thereto she prayed him that he send her again by this messenger all his heart for token.

When Tristram gat these tidings of the lady whom most he loved he was heavy and sorrowful thereof. He might not be glad of heart till he had seen the corselet Ysolt was clad withal and she would not remove it from her back till he should come again into the land. Then he spake to Kaherdin and they went straight unto England to win hazards and adventures. As churls were they clothed, and their faces painted and their raiment disguised, that none might know their secret; and they came unto the King's court and spake privily and did much of their will.

At a certain court the King held, great was the press that came there. After meat they went unto play and they began many games of fencing and wrestling: in all was Tristram master. Then they made a Welsh dance, and one that was hight "waveleis," and they brought challenges and hurled reeds and javelins and lances. Over all was Tristram prized, and after him Kaherdin passed the others in skill. But there was Tristram known and perceived by a friend, and he gave them two horses of price, there were none better in the land, for he was sore adoubted that they be not taken that day. In great jeopardy they put them and two lords they slew in that place. One was Cariadoc the fair; Kaherdin slew him in combat because that he had said that Kaherdin fled that other time when he departed. He hath well paid the avow that he made

in his accordment with Bringvain. Then they set
out in flight, to save their both lives They went,
these fellows, spurring down to the se ward. The
Cornish men sued them but they lost the n as at that
time. Within the forest Tristram and l aherdin set
them upon the road and wandered over the byways
of the wilderness and thereby they saved hemselves.
Then they went straight to Brittany: glac were they
of their vengeance.

Lords, this history is full various, and herefore
have I accorded it in my rhymes, and I sa thereof
so much as needeth, and I will put aside th : super-
fluity, for I would not tell in accord overmuch Here
is the matter at variance: of those that ar wont
to recount and tell the tale of Tristram, they speak
thereof diversely. From many men have I heard the
tale, and well I know what each telleth and eke
what they have set in scripture, but so far as I have
heard, they tell it not after Breri, which knew the
gests and the tales of all the kings and all the earls
that have been in Britain. As touching these tales
many of us will not grant in especial that which they
are wont to tell of the dwarf whose wife Kaherdin
should love: the dwarf should wound Tristram and
poison him with mickle craft, after that he hath
done damage unto Kaherdin, and by reason of this
wound and this damage should Tristram send
Governal to England for Ysolt. But I, Thomas,
will not grant this and will show by reason that this
might not be. For this Governal was known of all
and it was known through all the realm that he was

partner of their loves and a messenger unto Ysolt. The King hated him right sore and caused his people watch him. How then might he come to proffer his service at court unto the King, the barons, and the sergeants as he had been a strange merchant, without that a man so known should not be right soon espied? I wot not how he might save himself nor how he might bring away Ysolt. Certes, they have erred from the tale and departed from the truth, and if they will not yield this, I will not strive with them: let them hold unto theirs and I unto mine: reason will try all things well.

Chapter xciv

TO Brittany then they repaired them joyously, Tristram and Kaherdin, and they disported them gladly with their friends and their people, and went often to hunt in the forest and to tourney in the marches. They bare the renown and the pris of chivalry and of honor above all them of the country; and when they would go for to sojourn, they would go unto the groves to behold the fair images. On those images they had delight as of the ladies they so loved. By day they had solace there to pay for the loneliness they endured by night.

On a day they were gone on hunting until they should return: their fellows were ridden afore them, and save them twain no man was there. They were overpassing the Blanche Lande, and they looked to the right to the seaward, and they were ware of a knight coming: full richly was he harnessed, and he had a shield of gold fretted with vair, and of the same tincture were his spear and his pennon and his cognizance. By a path he cometh a wallop, covered by his shield and closed. Tall was he and big and right stout, and he was armed as a good knight. Tristram and Kaherdin waited his coming upon the road, and much they marveled who he might be. He cometh toward them thereas he seeeth them and saluteth them full sweetly: and Tristram saluteth him again and demandeth where he goeth and what errand and what haste he had.

"Sir," then said the knight, "can ye teach me unto the castle of Tristram l'Amerous?"

Tristram said: "Whom would ye? who been ye? what name have ye? Well will we teach you unto his abode, and if ye would have speech of Tristram, needeth you not go further, for Tristram am I cleped. Tell me now what ye desire?"

"I am right glad of this knowledge. I have to my name Tristram the Dwarf. I am of the marches of Brittany and upon the right I march upon the Spanish Sea. There have I a castle and a fair lady, the which I love as I do my life. But by great mischief have I lost her, for two nights agone she was stolen from me. Estult l'Orgulous of Castel Fer hath led her away with force and holdeth her in his castle and doth with her that seemeth him good. Such heartly sorrow have I thereof that almost I perish of the woe and dolor and grief: I know not what under heaven I should do. I may not have solace without her, and sith I have lost my disport, my joy, and all my bliss, my life is unto me little worth. Sir Tristram, I have heard say that he that loseth that most he desireth, to him is the remnant little boot. Never have I heard erst of such shrewd sorrow. Now ye be feared and sore dreaded and in all things the best knight and the noblest and the justest and the greatest lover of all that have lived ever. I cry you of mercy, Sir, and beseech your kindness and pray that ye come with me on this business and win me my leman again. Homage will I do you and fealty an ye succor me in this deed."

Then said Tristram: "Unto my power will I surely succor you, my friend, but go we now unto mine hostel. Tomorn will we dress us, and so will we perform this business."

When the knight heard that he put in delay the day, he said for wrath: "By my faith, my friend, ye are not he that beareth such fame. I wot an ye had been Tristram, the dolor that I feel ye had felt, for so hath Tristram loved that he knoweth well the woes that lovers endure. Had Tristram heard my lament, he had succored me in this love, nor had he prolonged such pain and such anguish. Whosoever ye be, fair friend, meseemeth never ye have loved, for an ye had known what love is, ye had had ruth of my sorrow. Who hath never known what love is, neither may he know what sorrow is, and ye, friend, that have no ways loved, may not feel my sorrow, for then had ye comen with me. God be with you. I will go seek Tristram that I may find him. None comfort shall I have but it be of him. Never was I so dismayed. O God, wherefore may I not die sith I have lost that w; ch most I desire? Liefer would I list to die, for I sh. ll have no pleasure nor comfort nor joy in mine h art sith I have lost through this ravishing that whicl I most love."

So complained him Tristram the vvarf and he was at point to go with their leave; bu the other Tristram had pity of him and said: "Fair sir, tarry now. With good reason have ye shown th t it behoveth me go with you sith that I am Tristram l'Amerous, and I will go blithely. Suffer ye that I send for mine arms."

Chapter xcv

HE sent for his arms and arrayed him and returned with Tristram the Dwarf, and they went to await and slay Estult l'Orgulous of Castel Fer. They toiled and wandered till that they found his strong castle, and in a border of a wood they alight and waited adventures. Estult l'Orgulous was full fierce: six brethren he had for knights, hardy and brave and full worthy, but he passed them all of valor. Now of the brethren twain were returning from a tournament, and in the wood the two Tristrams lay in a bushment, and suddenly they cried them defiance and hurled upon them right heavily.

There were these two brethren slain, and their cry
arose over all the land. Their lord heard their call,
and they of the castle mounted and encountered with
the two Tristrams and eagerly assailed them. Right
good knights were they as to the manner they used
their weapons, and as knights hardy and proved they
defended them against all and stinted not of their
fighting ere that they had slain the four. Natheless
was Tristram the Dwarf fallen dead, and the other
Tristram wounded through the loin of a sword that
was empoisoned. In his heat well he avenged him,
for he slew him that wounded him. Thus are all
the seven brethren destroyed, one Tristram dead,
and the other ill bestead, for he had a sore wound
of his body.

Chapter xcvi

WITH mickle torment he turned him again for
the pain that seized him, but so much he enforced himself that he arrived at his hostel and let
dress his wounds and let seek a leech for to help
him. They caused many to come unto him, but none
might heal him of that venom, for they had no
knowledge of it and then were they all deceived;
they could not make a plaster that might cast or
draw it forth. Roots enow they beat and bruised
and culled grasses and made leechdoms but they
might not aid him nothing. Tristram doth naught
but wax worse. The venom spread through his

body and made it swell within and without: he blackened and discolored and lost his strength and his bones appeared full clearly. Then he understood well that he should lose his life if he had not aid most speedily and he saw that none might warish him and therefore needs must he die. He knew no heal unto his malady; natheless if Queen Ysolt wist that this strong evil was upon him and were with him, she would well recover him. But he may not go unto her nor endure the travail of the sea, and he was greatly adoubted of the country, for there had he many enemies, nor might Ysolt come unto him. He knew not how he might have heal. In his heart he had great sorrow, for sorely his languor grieved him and his pain and the stench of the wound. He moaned sore and waxed right feeble, for much the venom tormented him.

Privily he sent for Kaherdin, and to him would he discover his woe, for Kaherdin's love was set upon him. He caused to void the chamber there he lay, and he would not suffer that any abode in the house for that communication but them twain. Ysolt marveled much in her heart what it should be that he would do, whether he would forsake the world and become a monk or canon: sore she was abashed. Withoutforth his chamber but beside the wall night unto his bed, she went and stood, for she purposed her to listen their counsel. To one that was her familiar she assigned to watch, while she stood beside the wall. Tristram was so feebled that he lay against the wall: Kaherdin sat by his side.

Piteously they wept both and bemoaned their goodly fellowship that was so soon dissevered, their love and great friendship: they had heartly sorrow and pity, anguish and teen and woe: each for other sorrowed: they wept and made great dole that their love must needs sunder; full fine and loyal had it been. Tristram called Kaherdin:

"Hearken, fair friend. I am in a strange land and here have I had nor friend nor kinsman, fair fellow, but thee only. Never have I had delight nor mirth save of thy solace. Now well do I surmise that if I were in mine own land, I might with knowledge be healed, but sith I have here no succor, I shall lose, fair sweet friend, my life. Without help I must needs die, for no man may me heal save only Queen Ysolt. She may do it an she will: the leechdom hath she and the cunning and the will, if she but knew my case. Fair fellow, I know not what to do, by what device she may have knowledge of it. For well I wot an she had wist thereof, of my malady she could help me and by her knowledge heal my wound. But how may she come? If I wist who might go thither and bear her my message, some good rede she would give me when she understood my great need. So surely I trust her that I wot well she would not withhold her from naught to aid me in this distress, for unto me she hath full stable love. I wot not, for sooth, how to advise me, and for this cause, my fellow, I require thee, for thy friendship and large pity, undertake this service for me. Perform for me this message for

[269]

sake of our fellowship and the faith thou sworest upon thine hand that time Ysolt bestowed upon thee Bringvain. And I make thee faithfully mine avow that if thou undertake this voyage for me, thy man will I become and love thee above all thing."

Kaherdin beheld Tristram weeping and heard him groan and despair, and had in his heart passing great ruth thereof and sweetly answered for his love and said: "Fair fellow, weep not and I will do whatsomever thou wilt. Certes, friend, for to heal thee would I bring me full nigh unto death and in jeopardy of death to purchase thee comfort. For sake of the loyalty I owe thee, naught shall remain unto me, neither naught that I may do nor distress nor pain, that I shall not do my power to do thy will in all things. Say what thou list have me fetch again from her and I will go to make me ready thereto."

Tristram answered: "Gramercy. Now hearken what I say. Take with thee this ring: it is the token betwixt us: and when thou shalt have come unto Mark's court, fare thou as a merchant and carry good cloths of silk. Cause her to see the ring, and when she shall see it and know thee, she will use sleights and crafts to speak with thee at leisure. Tell her I desire for her so much weal that none without her remaineth in me: from mine heart I send her such weal that none abideth with me. My heart's greeting unto her is weal, but save by her goodwill never will weal return unto me. I send her all my weal. Comfort shall never be vouchsafed me, nor weal of life nor health, if they be not brought by her. If she bring me not again my weal and recomfort me not with her mouth, my health will remain with her, and I shall die in my great anguish. In fine, say that I am but dead if I have not comfort of her. Show her well my sorrow and the malady whereof I wax feeble and that she come to solace me. Tell her that now she remember her of the joys and the delights that sometime we used, both day and night; of the great pains and the great woes; of the pleasures and the sweets of our high love and true, whenas she erst healed my wound; of the drink that we drank together on the sea whenas we were seized of love. In that drink was our death, and never have we had solace thereof: in the hour it was given us we drank our death. Let her remember of my griefs that I have suffered for love. I have lost all my kin, mine uncle the King, and his people: with shame was I flemed and exiled into other lands: such pain and travail have I suffered that unnethe I live and little am I worth. Our love and our desire none may never divide: anguish nor pain nor sorrow may never divide our love, for whenever they strove most to divide it, least they sped. Our bodies they dissevered, but love might they not banish. Let her remember of the covenant she made at the sundering in the garden when I departed from her, and when she betaught me this ring and told me that whatsomever land I repaired me into, never should I love other than her. Never have I had love toward other nor may I love thy sister: nor her nor another might I love as much as I love the Queen. So hotly I love Queen Ysolt that thy sister abideth a maiden. Summon her by her good faith that she come unto me in this need. Now let it appear if ever she have loved me. What she hath afore done will little avail me if in my need she will not help me and counsel me against this sorrow. What will her love help me if now she fail me in my sorrow. I wot not of what boot our passion may be if in my great need now it fail. Little hath all her solace availed if she will not aid me to health. Kaherdin, I know not what to pray thee beyond this that I now require. Govern you as ye best may, and greet Bringvain well for me. Show the Queen the malady I have: an God heed not, thereof shall I die. Long may I not live in the teen and the torment that I feel. My fellow, bethink thee how thou mayst hasten and return to me swiftly, for if thou return not most swiftly, wit thou well thou wilt see me never. XL days hast thou of respite: if thou do that I have said and if Ysolt come with thee, look well that no man wot thereof but us. Hide it from thy sister that hath a deeming of this love: thou shalt cause Ysolt be held for a leechwoman, comen for to heal my wound. Thou shalt take my fair ship and carry within it two sails: the one shall be white, the other black. An thou mayst compass it that Ysolt come for to heal my wound, on thy return use the white sail: if thou bring Ysolt not, sail thou with the black sail. I know not more to tell thee, friend. God, our Lord, guide thee and bring thee again safe and whole."

Therewith he sighed and wept and lamented; and Kaherdin wept with him and kissed Tristram and took his leave. He went to make ready his voyage: with the first wind he took the sea. They hauled up the anchor, hoisted the sail, and sailed forth with a soft wind and clave the waves and billows, the tall seas and the deep. He took fair bachelors and carried cloth of silk wrought of strange colors, and rich vessels of Tours, and wines of Poitou, and hawks of Spain, for to hide and cover his errand, how he might come at Ysolt, for whom Tristram maketh such dole. He clave the sea with his ship, and ran under sail toward England. A score days and a score nights hath he run ere he came unto the isle and might arrive thereas he should hear somewhat touching Ysolt.

The wrath of women is much to dread: much ought each man take heed thereto, for thereas she hath loved most, there soonest will she take vengeance. As readily their love cometh, so readily cometh their hate, and longer dureth their rancor when it cometh than doth their love. They can well love within measure, but their hatred they attemper nothing when they been in wrath. But I dare not tell my thought on this matter, for it concerneth me not at all. Ysolt as Blanches Mains stood by the wall and listened and heard Tristram's language; well hath she caught every word and thus she won knowledge of his love. In her heart she was wroth out of measure that she had loved Tristram so, when he was turned unto another: now was it made full plain why she had lost her pleasaunce of him. That she had heard well she cherished but made semblaunt as she had wist naught. But so soon as she had occasion, passing cruelly would she wreak her on the thing that of the world most she loved. Right so soon as the doors were opened, Ysolt entered the chamber and made him right fair countenance as lover oweth unto lover: full sweetly she spake unto him and kissed him oft and clipped him and showeth him passing fair love. But in her anger she studied evil, by what mean she might be avenged, and ofttimes she demanded and inquired when Kaherdin should return with the leech should heal him: but of no kind intent she complained. The felony that she cast to accomplish an she might, abode in her heart, for wrath moved her thereto.

In the meanwhile Kaherdin sailed forth to sea and stinted not of his sailing till he came unto the land where he went to seek the Queen. It was the mouth of the Thames: he went further with his merchandise, but in the mouth withoutforth the entrance he anchored his ship in an haven: in a cog he went forthright unto London above the bridge. There he unpacked his merchandise and he unfolded and opened his cloths of silk. London is a right rich city, a better is not in Christendom, nor a worthier nor a better esteemed nor a better garnished of rich folk. Much they love largess and honor, and lead their life in great pleasaunce. It is the health of England and beyond it needeth no man to seek. At the wall's foot floweth the Thames, and there cometh the merchandise of all lands where Christian merchants go. There eke be men of mickle wisdom. Thither came Lord Kaherdin with his cloths and his hawks, whereof he had both good and fair. On his fist he took a great goshawk and a cloth of strange color and a cup well wrought, for it was chased and enameled. He made of them a present unto King Mark and said courteously that he was come to this land with his goods to gain and win for himself other goods: may he grant him peace in his realm that he may not be assailed nor have damage nor shame of chamberlain or sheriff. The King vouchsafed unto him a siker peace, in hearing of all the court. Kaherdin went to the Queen for to speak and to show her of his wares: a brooch wrought of fine gold he bare in hand: none better I ween was in the world: he made proffer thereof unto the Queen.

"The gold is right good," he said.

Never had Ysolt seen better. Then he took Tristram's ring from his finger and set it beside the other and said:

"Queen, behold now: this gold is brighter of hue than is the gold of this ring: yet I count the ring fair."

When the Queen espied the ring, she knew Kaherdin straightway: her heart changed and her color, and she sighed for great woe, and feared to hear tidings. She called Kaherdin apart and asked him, would he sell the ring, and what thing he would take for it, and if he had other merchandise. All this did she for subtlety, for that she would deceive her wardens. Kaherdin was alone with Ysolt.

"Lady," said he, "now listen what I shall say and hold it in mind. Tristram as thy lover sendeth thee his love and service and greeting as unto his lady and his love, in which dwelleth his death and his life. Thy liegeman is he and lover: unto thee he hath sent me in his need. He sendeth word that never will he have comfort in this death if not by thee, nor will he have weal of life nor health an they be not brought by thee. He is wounded unto death of a sword that was poisoned: no leech may we find that can to medicine this malady, and now are the leeches in such amaze that all his body is in evil case. He languisheth and liveth in woe and anguish, and foully he smelleth. He sendeth thee word that he will not live if he have not thy succor, and therefore he sendeth unto thee by me and summoneth thee by that faith and loyalty thou owest him, Ysolt, that for naught in the world thou leave not to come to him, sith never afore he hath had need, and therefore behoveth thee not refuse it. Remember thee now of the great love and the pains and woes that ye twain have endured together. He loseth his life and his youth, and for thee hath he been banished and ofttimes chased from the realm. He hath lost King Mark: bethink thee of the damage he hath had thereof. Behoveth thee remember the covenant that was made betwixt you at the sundering in the garden, where thou kissed him when thou gavest him this ring and thou behote him thy love. Have pity of him, lady. An thou succor him not now, certes, never wilt thou give him heal. Therefore behoveth thee come, for else may he not live. This message he sendeth thee loyally, and for token he sendeth thee this ring: keep it, he giveth it thee."

When Ysolt heareth his message, she is anguished of heart and hath pain and ruth and sorrow: never erst had she greater. She museth much and sigheth and desireth Tristram, her lover, but she knoweth not how to go. She goeth to speak with Bringvain, and telleth her all the adventure of the poisoning of the wound and of the pain that he hath and the grief, and how that he lieth in languor, and how and by whom he hath sent for her, or his wound will never be healed more. She hath shown all this misery, and then she taketh counsel what she may do. Now beginneth in the speech that they hold sighing and wailing and weeping and pain and great heaviness and woe and teen by reason of the pity they had unto him. Natheless they said and took counsel in speech that they should make ready their voyage and go with Kaherdin to give counsel touching Tristram's sickness and to help him in his stern need. They made them ready against evening and took that they would have. When all the rest slept, secretly that night they departed, right cunningly yet with great jeopardy, by a postern of the wall that stood above Thames. At the mounting of the tide the water came there: the cog was all ready and the Queen entered within. They rowed and sailed with the ebb, and swiftly they departed with the wind. Much they enforced themselves to labor, and they stinted not of their rowing until that they came unto the great ship. They hoisted sail and departed. As far as the wind might carry them they ran over the sea, coasting the strange land past the haven of Wissant and past Boulogne and past Treport. The wind was driving and strong and the ship that bare them, light. They passed by Normandy and joyously now they sailed and blithely, for they had a wind after their will.

Chapter xcvii

TRISTRAM, that lay abed of his wound, languished with woe, and of naught might he have solace: leechdom might not avail him, and naught that he doth aideth him. He longeth for Ysolt's coming and he coveteth none other thing. Without her he may have no boot, and for her only he liveth thus long. He feebleth and waiteth her in his bed and hopeth that she should come and recover his malady and believeth that without her he may not live. All the day he sendeth unto the shore to espy if the ship returneth: none other desire he holdeth in his heart, and oft he maketh to bear and set his bed beside the sea to wait and behold the ship, how it saileth and with what sail. Unto naught hath he desire but of her coming, and this is all his thought and hope and will. What he hath on earth he accounteth for naught if the Queen come not unto him. Oft he maketh carry him again for the fear that he feareth, because that he dreadeth that she come not nor hold not faith with him: liefer would he hear this from another than to behold the ship come without her. He longeth for to see the ship, yet he would not wit no failure. In his heart he feareth, and yet longeth to behold her. Often he plaineth him unto his wife, but uttereth not his desire, save of Kaherdin, that cometh not. So long he tarrieth that much he feareth that he hath not sped in the business.

Hearken now a piteous malfortune and adventure full dolorous and piteous unto all lovers: never heard ye dolefuller chance of such desire and such love. Where Tristram waiteth Ysolt, Ysolt would fain arrive, and so nigh hath she come unto the shore that they espy land and are glad and sail merrily. But from the south leapeth upon them a wind and smiteth the ship afore in middes of the sail that it maketh the whole vessel turn about. The sailors run to windward and turn the sail, but whatsomever their desire may be, they return. The wind enforceth itself and raiseth the waves, the sea that is deep is stirred, the weather darkeneth, the air thickeneth, the billows heave, the sea blackeneth, there falleth rain and sleet and the storm increaseth, the bowlines and ropes break. They lower the sail and drive before the wind, steering with the waves and the wind. They have set their cog in the sea, for that they were nigh unto their own country, but in evil hour have they forgotten it, for a billow hath it toshivered. Moreover they have now lost so much and the tempest hath so increased that there was no mariner so strong he might stand on his feet. All wept and all bewailed them and for terror they made dole out of measure. Then said Ysolt:

"Alas, woe is me! God permitteth not that I live long enow to behold Tristram, my love: He willeth that I were drowned in the sea! Tristram, had I but spoken with you, I had not recked if then I died. Fair love, when ye will hear of my death, well I wot ye will nevermore have solace. Of my death will ye take such sorrow to increase the great feebleness ye have that ye may not be healed. My coming lieth no longer within my power; an God had willed and I had arrived, I should attend upon your malady, for no sorrow have I else but that ye have no succor. This is my sorrow and anguish, and in my heart am I right heavy that thou wilt have no remedy against thy death, love, when I die. Naught is my death unto me: whenas God willeth it, I will it well. But so soon as ye will hear of it, I wot well ye will die. Of such fashion is our love I may not feel sorrow without you: ye may not die without me, nor may I perish without you. If I must suffer wreck at sea, then beseemeth you in like wise to drown: ye may not drown on land: ye ought to come seek me at sea. I perceive ye shall die afore me, and well I know that ye must die soon. Love, I fail of my desire, for in thine arms I had hoped to die and to be buried in a tomb, but we have now failed therein. But even yet it may so befall, for if I must drown

here, ye also, I trow, ought to drown, and one fish
may devour us both: so by adventure may we have,
fair love, one sepulchre, for well may some man
take the fish and will know our bodies and will do
them great honor as beseemeth our love. But what
I say may not be. Yea, but if God will, so must it
be. What would ye seek, love, on the sea? I wot
not what ye would do there, but there am I and
there shall die. I shall drown therein without you,
Tristram. Then is it, fair sweet, soft comfort unto
me that ye will not know of my death. Without this
place will it never be heard, and I know not, love,
any that should tell it you. After me long will ye
live and await my coming. By God's will ye may
be healed. That is the thing I most desire, and
more I covet your heal than I list to arrive. For
unto you I have so fine love, my love, that I ought
rather to be afeard that when after my death ye are
healed ye forget me in your life, Tristram, or have
solace of other woman after my death. Certes,
love, of Ysolt as Blanches Mains at least I dread
me and fear. I wot not if I ought to fear her, but
wit ye well, an ye were dead afore me, I should live
but a short season after you. Certes, I know not
what beseemeth me to do, but I desire you above
all things. God grant us either to come together
that I may heal you, love, or to die, us twain, of
one anguish."

Chapter xcviii

THUS while her torment endured, Ysolt wailed and lamented her. More than five days the storm lasted and the foul weather; then fell the wind and the weather was fair. They hoisted up the white sail and sailed with right good speed so that Kaherdin espied Brittany. Then were they glad and jocund and merry, and drew the sail full high that it might be seen from afar whether it were white or black. From afar would Kaherdin show that color: it was the last day that Lord Tristram had assigned them that they should return from England. While they sailed gladly, the heat waxed and the wind fell that they might not sail. Full soft and smooth was the sea. Nor here nor there their ship stirred save as the wave drew it, nor had they more their cog. Now was there great distress. Near before them they saw the land, but they have not wind they may attain it withal. Hither and thither they went drifting, now forward now backward: they may not advance their voyage, and passing great was their hardship. Ysolt was tormented sore thereby: she perceived the land she had coveted, but might not attain unto it. Wellnigh she died of her longing. Within the ship they desired land, but the wind blew ever softly. Oft Ysolt called herself wretched. They wished the ship at the strand, but they saw it now no more.

YSOLT VOYAGETH UNTO TRISTRAM

Chapter xcix

TRISTRAM was heavy and woeful, and moaned oft and sighed for Ysolt, which he so desired: his eyen wept, his body writhed, and wellnigh he perished for desire. In this anguish and woe came his wife Ysolt before him, intending great treason and said:

"My love, Kaherdin now cometh. His ship have I beheld on the sea; unnethe have I seen it sailing, but yet I have so beheld it that I know it for his. God grant he bring such tidings whereof ye shall have comfort of heart."

Tristram starteth up at those tidings and saith unto Ysolt: "Fair love, know ye for sooth it is his ship? Now tell me, what is the sail?"

Thus saith Ysolt: "I know it sikerly. Wit ye well the sail is altogether black. They have hoisted it and drawn it high, for that the wind faileth them."

Then hath Tristram such sharp anguish that never had he nor would have greater, and he turneth him unto the wall and saith: "God save Ysolt and me. Sith ye would not come unto me, behoveth me die for your love. I may no longer hold my life. For you I die, Ysolt, fair love. Ye have no pity on my feebleness, but of my death will ye have woe. It is to me great solace, love, that ye will have pity of my death." Thrice hath he said: "Ysolt, my love." At the fourth he yielded up his spirit.

Chapter c

THEN throughout the house they wept, the knights and the fellows: the noise was loud and the lamentation great. Knights and sergeants went forth and bare the body from the bed and laid it upon a cloth of samite and covered it with a pall of ray. On the sea the wind hath risen and striketh in the middes of the sail and driveth the ship unto land. Ysolt issueth from the ship and heareth the great laments in the street, and the bells in the minsters and the chapels, and asketh of men what tidings, and wherefore they make such ringing and wherefore such weeping befalleth. An ancient man then saith:

"Fair lady, so God me help, we have here great sorrow that never people had a greater. Tristram, the noble and proved, is dead. He was a solace unto all this realm. He gave largess to the poor and great aid to the wretched. Even now hath he died in his bed of a wound he had in his body. Never such misadventure befell this region."

As soon as Ysolt hath heard the tidings, for woe she may not utter a word, of his death she is so dolorous. Lifting her robe she goeth up the street afore the others into the palace. The Bretons saw never woman of her beauty: they marvel through the city whence she cometh and what she is.

THE DIRGE IS SUNG OVER TRISTRAM

Chapter ci

YSOLT goeth thereas she seeth the body and turneth her unto the east and prayeth for him piteously: "Tristram, my love, whenas I see thee dead, of reason I should not live. Dead art thou for my love, and I die, love, for pity, sith I might not come in time for to heal thee and thy wound. My love, my love, for thy death nevermore shall I have comfort of naught, nor joy nor pleasure nor delight. Cursed be the tempest that tarried me so long at sea, my love, that I might not come. An I had come in time, I had given thee life and spoken sweetly unto thee of the love that was between us: I had bemoaned our fortune, our bliss, our pleasaunce, and the pain and the great anguish that hath been of our love: and I had rehearsed this and kissed thee and clipped thee. An I had not power to heal thee, then had we died together. Sith now I might not come in time and I wist not thy plight and am come unto thy death, of the same drink shall I have solace. For me thou hast lost thy life, and I shall do as true lover should: for thee will I die and with thee."

She embraced him and stretched herself, kissed his mouth and face, and right straightly she clung to him, and stretched her body to his body, and laid her mouth to his mouth. Then she yielded up her spirit and died here beside him for sorrow of her lover. Tristram died for longing, Ysolt for that

[289]

she came too late. Tristram died for love, and the fair Ysolt for pity.

Here Thomas endeth his scripture. He giveth to all lovers greeting, to the wretched and the amorous, to the jealous and the desirous, to the blithe and the despairing, to all those that will hear these verses. If I have not spoken wholly after their will, I have said the best unto my power, and I have told all the truth even as I promised at the first, and words and verses have I preserved. For an ensample have I done this and for to garnish this history that it should please lovers, and that here and there they might find somewhat they might remember, and that they might have thereof great solace malgre change, malgre wrong, malgre pain, malgre tears, malgre all the wiles of love.

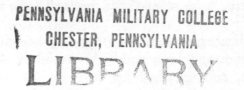

Bibliographical Note

A VIRTUALLY complete bibliography of the Tristram legend up to 1939 is Heinz Küpper's *Bibliographie zur Tristansage*, Jena, 1941 (*Deutsche Arbeiten der Universität Köln*, Vol. XVII); to be supplemented by J. Horrent's review in *Revue Belge de Philologie et d'Histoire*, 1944, p. 357. An excellent selective and critical bibliography of the legend and of the French texts by Helaine Newstead is to be found in *Critical Bibliography of French Literature*, Vol. I, ed. by U. T. Holmes, Syracuse Univ. Press, 1947, pp. 119–30. J. van Dam gave a good survey of the problems in *Neophilologus*, XV (1929–30), 18, 88, 183. The illustrations of the legend in medieval art are covered in R. S. and L. H. Loomis, *Arthurian Legends in Medieval Art*, New York, 1938. Among the more recent publications of value should be mentioned: Béroul, *Roman de Tristan*, ed. by E. Muret, rev. L.–M. Defourques, 4th ed., Paris, 1947; *Folie Tristan d'Oxford*, ed. by E. Hoepffner, 2d ed., Paris, 1943; G. Frank, "Marie de France and the Tristram Legend," *PMLA*, LXIII (1948), 405; Gottfried von Strassburg, *Tristan und Isolt*, ed. by A. Closs, 2d rev. ed., Oxford, 1947, containing a useful introduction; *The "Tristan and Isolde" of Gottfried von Strassburg*, selected passages trans. and ed. by E. H.

[291]

Bibliographical Note

Zeydel, Princeton, N.J., 1948; M. Heimerle, *Gottfried und Thomas; ein Vergleich*, 1942 (Frankfurter Quellen und Forschungen, XXXI); J. Horrent, "La Composition de la Folie Tristan de Berne," *Revue Belge de Philologie et d'Histoire*, 1946–47, p. 21; P. Jonin, "La Vengeance chez l'Iseut de Béroul et chez l'Iseut de Thomas," *Neophilologus*, XXXIII (1949), 207; H. Newstead, "Kaherdin and the Enchanted Pillow," *PMLA*, LXV (1950), 290; S. Singer, "Thomas von Britannien und Gottfried von Strassburg," *Tieche Festschrift* (Bern, 1947); A. Pauphilet, *Le Legs du Moyen Age* (Melun, 1950), pp. 107–41; B. H. Wind, "Quelques remarques sur la versification du Tristan de Thomas," *Neophilologus*, XXXIII (1949), 85. Dr. Wind has also published a new edition of Thomas's poem, and Professor Newstead is making a thorough study of the sources and development of the legend.

In view of the wide circulation of Denis de Rougement's *L'Amour et l'Occident*, translated and published in England as *Passion and Society* and in the United States as *Love in the Western World*, it is necessary to state that there is no trace in the Tristram romances of Celtic mythology or of Albigensian heresy, and that nothing could be more absurd than the notion that Tristram and Ysolt were in love, not with each other, but with death.

On the subject of courtly love consult C. Dawson, *Mediaeval Religion and Other Essays*, New York, 1934, pp. 123–54; S. Painter, *French Chivalry*, Baltimore, 1940, pp. 95–148; Andreas Capellanus,

Bibliographical Note

Art of Courtly Love, trans. by J. J. Parry, New York, 1941; E. Power, in C. G. Crump and E. F. Jacob, *Legacy of the Middle Ages*, Oxford, 1938, pp. 401–17. On Eleanor of Aquitaine and her influence consult A. Kelly, *Eleanor of Aquitaine and the Four Kings*, Cambridge, Mass., 1950.

[293]